CW00553399

Guide to capital cost estimating

Fourth edition

17

Guide to capital cost estimating

Fourth edition

Edited by A.M. Gerrard

Published by
Institution of Chemical Engineers (IChemE),
Davis Building,
165–189 Railway Terrace,
Rugby, Warwickshire CV21 3HQ, UK
A Registered Charity

© 2000 Institution of Chemical Engineers
Third Edition 1988

ISBN 0 85295 399 2

Printed in the United Kingdom by Bell & Bain Limited, Glasgow

Preface to the fourth edition

The purposes of this revised edition are, as always, to aid student engineers in the design activities, which they undertake during their courses, and to help young engineers in industry to compile their own set of cost data.

Although much of the material in the third edition has been retained, the major changes are the new cost data included in Chapter 7 and the updating of the cost index information in Chapter 8. Of course, an academic cannot create cost data; it has to be donated by industrialists. For this, I am most grateful to Mr G. Russell of Baker Mallett, Stockton-on-Tees, Mr G. Wilkinson of BASF, Middlesbrough and Mr M. Ellis of Foster Wheeler, Reading and others who wish to remain anonymous. Without their generosity, a fourth edition would not exist.

Three members of the third edition Working Party offered their time again. Dr R.A. Betts and Mr L.F. Williams contributed many useful comments and Professor A.V. Bridgwater updated his sections in Chapter 4 on short-cut estimating techniques. In addition, P. Chow and A. Abbas analysed the raw data as part of their studies here at Teesside. All their efforts are appreciated.

The data should be viewed as an approximate guide to the costs of items. Readers should collect their own data which are relevant to their situation wherever possible, but if you are stuck, start here! Remember that the prices quoted by equipment manufacturers will be influenced by their supply and demand position and that all point forecasts of cost are inaccurate, so do try to give a probable range in your final figures.

I hope that the material presented here is useful.

Dr A.M. Gerrard
University of Teesside
Middlesbrough

Acknowledgements to the third edition

The membership of the Working Party established by the Institution of Chemical Engineers and the Association of Cost Engineers, who prepared the third edition of this Guide, comprised:

B.A.J. Jones (Chairman and Assistant Editor)
Commonwealth Development Corporation

Dr R.A. Betts	University of Birmingham
Dr A.V. Bridgwater	University of Aston
A.T.H. Calway	Foster Wheeler Energy Ltd
D.J. George (Editor)	Cremer and Warner
K.A.R. Julian	APV Projects Ltd
K. Sutherland	Chemical Engineering Developments Ltd
Dr G.L. Wells	University of Sheffield
L.F. Williams	Humphreys and Glasgow Ltd
F.M. Dendy (Secretary)	Institution of Chemical Engineers

Contents

Introduction

1

Money does matter in engineering. Along with safety, health and environmental concerns, financial considerations help to give us a way of deciding what is likely to be the best course of action in a project. This book is concerned primarily with capital cost estimation, but the importance of operating costs in both profitability analyses and optimization studies must not be ignored. As mentioned in the preface, the ideas of uncertainty should never be far from our minds. Even so, we have to start somewhere, and a (point) forecast of an item's cost within a total plant complex is a reasonable first objective.

The structure of the Guide is straightforward. Chapter 2 looks at the development of a project starting from an early R and D investigation to the production of a detailed design. Chapter 3 then suggests the sorts of estimating techniques appropriate to each stage of this process.

Chapter 4 outlines the principles of costing methodology using step counting, power law (or exponential) relationships and the use of various factorial approaches. Many up-to-date short-cut correlations, along with a useful set of installation and bulk item factors (for piping, instrumentation and so on) are included.

Chapter 5 gives additional material on styles of presenting the overall plant cost information and it offers further ideas on contingency levels, including a useful checklist. The importance of working capital, scrap valuation and commissioning costs are also included. Chapter 6 suggests various ways in which the costing activities can influence the overall process economics.

Chapter 7 contains new information on the costs of main plant items plus a selection of data on bulk item costing. The updating of costs arising from the passage of time or for different locations in different currencies is handled in Chapter 8. The Guide closes with a brief listing of other sources of information and a glossary of commonly-used terms.

If you are an industrialist who wants to cost items, you should go to Chapter 7 first and then to Chapter 4 to obtain an overall plant cost. For those costing a plant at the R and D stage, Chapter 4 will be useful. Students can read it all, starting here ...

Project development

2

2.1 Introduction

By far the most important purpose of capital cost estimation is to provide the means whereby decisions can be taken on the development of new projects or the extending or revamping of existing plants. Once such a project is approved, the cost estimate, after suitable refinement, becomes a yardstick against which the total project progress is measured, and the venture's success may be judged. For the large number of engineers employed by manufacturers, contractors or consultants to prepare estimates, it is a vital part of their jobs.

2.2 Time and cost – the balance

In order to assist young engineers to appreciate their role in a new venture and to enable them to make the greatest contribution to its success, it is necessary for them to understand something of the manner in which a new project is developed in a commercial organization and the vital influence of time during all steps of this development[1]. An immediate concern is likely to be the reliability of future production, first cost and operating cost estimates. However, improvements in any of these areas will usually require the allocation of further skilled, frequently scarce, manpower resources, and will often result in delay to the project. The balance of these factors is a matter for experienced judgement.

It should be understood that the same overall considerations apply whether the project involves the production of a new product by a manufacturing concern, or by a contractor working for the manufacturing industry, although there are considerable differences of detail between the approaches of these parties.

In recent years not only has the rate of technological innovation increased rapidly but this has been accompanied by sharp fluctuations in market conditions, interest rates, raw materials prices and, at times, rapid escalation of labour and materials costs. One immediate result of these factors is the increasing inability to make quantified predictions with any confidence for more than a limited period ahead. This is especially true when there are wide and rapid changes in currency exchange rates which have necessitated the careful choice of the currency to be used in any estimate or feasibility study.

It is rare for development effort to be justifiable, where it is aimed at achieving a near perfect design. Not only may the delay in reaching this design stage lead in most instances to higher capital costs, but the increasing imprecision caused by this delay on other relevant factors also makes this approach of questionable validity. Time-consuming and costly efforts by the design team to achieve 'elegance' or 'perfection' of design must be guarded against!

Feasibility studies arc oftcn carried out before development work is complete and, with increasing frequency, investment decisions are taken at this stage and funds are then released. Inaccuracies in estimating costs at this time are often less serious than errors in estimating the time to production. For this reason, it is important for the engineer to ensure that the time estimates submitted are as realistic as possible.

2.3 Feasibility studies and reports

All new capital projects involve the following phases:

- design;
- procurement;
- construction;
- commissioning.

Most companies appoint a project manager to ensure the effective co-ordination of these activities and of the many specialist departments (safety, accounts, legal and so on) who are directly and indirectly concerned. However, this manager is often not appointed until funds have been allocated, and in this case, the engineer preparing the feasibility study would be well advised to consult fully with an engineer who has such experience to ensure that the relevant factors are taken into account (see Chapter 5).

In developing the process flowsheet and layout, and particularly if this work has not yet been completed, the design engineer must be aware of the effects that decisions will have on the project timetable as well as the cost.

The value of using standardized items of equipment and fittings, and readily available materials of construction whenever practicable, cannot be over emphasized; these normally permit a choice of vendors and thus price competitiveness and some reliability in delivery dates. Special equipment, or items made of exotic construction materials, need to be designed, fabricated, proved and then sometimes modified with possibly disastrous effects on project timing. This would be the case when a large item is involved, which has many auxiliaries and is located centrally in a plant, where its late delivery would prevent progress on a substantial amount of other work on site.

These, and similar considerations, enable the engineer to submit a feasibility report where alternatives have been properly studied in respect of efficiency, cost, time and safety. The report is intended to demonstrate the technical and commercial viability of the proposed venture. The report should state on what assumptions the estimates of time are made and what the margins of error are likely to be, as these considerations may influence a decision. Time estimates for design and development and the parameters on which they are based are agreed upon with the relevant departments to ensure that they are realistic and can be met. Time control for the total project begins at this stage and must include the date for approval of funds, as time lost in this interval cannot be recovered later.

The amount of detail involved is a matter of company philosophy but it should always include a process flowsheet identifying main equipment items and their sizes, type and extent of control, instrumentation and materials of construction. The scale of manufacture and expansion potential are stated, as well as the demands on company resources of space (including storage), services and personnel. Operating costs include not only labour, materials and energy but also, where significant, items such as effluent treatment. Safety and environmental factors are also assessed (see also Chapter 5).

2.4 Project types

In the post-war era of rapid industrial growth, almost all project activity was devoted to new (and frequently large) projects. Two oil crises later, much has changed in this regard, and the present time sees a great deal of effort devoted to increased operating efficiency, energy conservation projects or plant redesign for safety or environmental reasons. This leads to widely differing types of capital project.

New, complete plants, although the most involved of all the project types, may also be relatively easy to estimate because of the absence of constraints otherwise imposed by trying to fit into an existing complex. Such projects include all the elements of cost estimating, from the purchase of the site to the provision of all the necessary utilities. The variation in scope is obviously wide — from a small batch plant costing, say, a fraction of a million pounds, up to a 'world-scale' bulk chemicals plant, such as ammonia-urea or methanol, costing hundreds of millions. Although the consequences of error increase with plant size, the skills involved and the complexity of the estimating task vary remarkably little over this wide range in plant cost.

Next in complexity (or in magnitude of the estimating task) come major plant extensions — either to increase the range of products, or to expand the production capacity. There will be some constraints on the design and cost estimating process because of the requirement to match the standards of the older plant, but these may be offset by the advantages of the availability of historical cost data (hopefully not too old) and of established contacts with equipment suppliers. Plant extensions frequently involve the construction of a duplicate to an existing line so that the cost exercise becomes similarly duplicated. Upstream or downstream extensions are more difficult, since the new plant items will presumably be different from those of the main plant.

Revamping projects generally arise because plants that have been in operation for some time have become outdated. The feed material might have changed (this being especially the case for petroleum refineries) causing the input stage of the plant to be modified to cater for the change. A more efficient piece of equipment may become available, and fitted into the existing plant ('retrofitted') perhaps with considerable changes to the flowsheet in order to accommodate it. Energy costs have changed a great deal, and the search for energy savings can lead to considerable changes within a plant — especially where a process integration study has been made — with a consequent need for new equipment. Considerable internal change may become necessary in order to increase safety standards to acceptable levels, while the tightening of environmental discharge criteria for the plant can create a requirement for new plant to treat an existing effluent or to change the process so as to reduce or prevent the formation of that effluent.

2.5 Project evaluation

As has already been implied, there are two prime purposes for a detailed cost estimate:

(a) to permit a decision to be taken on whether or not to proceed with a new plant or plant modification; and
(b) to support the allocation of funds to an approved project and then to control their subsequent disbursement.

(A third major purpose, that of preparing a tender by a contractor who is bidding for a particular project, usually against specific tender documents, should not be forgotten — it is of prime importance to the contractor.)

The first of these purposes becomes a component of the project evaluation process, and although this is the subject of a companion guide[2], the main elements of project evaluation need to be outlined here in order to illustrate the importance of the cost estimate.

A new project normally represents a potential investment by the owners of the enterprise, with the aim of obtaining a satisfactory return on that investment. Alternatively, the owners could put their money on deposit in the bank. The evaluation study has to show that the project will produce a better rate of return on the investment than could be achieved by leaving it in the bank. If this proves to be the case, then it is probable that the project will proceed. If the return is lower than the bank could produce (or not much greater) then implementation is unlikely, unless there are other strong reasons for proceeding such as ensuring the supply of a critical intermediate product for a later process.

The method used to determine the return produced by the proposed project is easy to describe. All the cost items are calculated and allocated to their appropriate time periods during the total life of the project. These costs include not only the obvious ones such as capital and operating costs, but also the less obvious ones such as the cost of financing any loans during plant construction, marketing the product, or waiting for the product to be paid for after it has been sold. The project's expected revenues are then similarly allocated, not forgetting the scrap value of the plant at the end of its life, and the release of working capital at the same time. Finally, the rate of interest is determined which would produce payments equivalent to the project's revenues from investments equivalent to the programme of costs.

This calculation is tedious if undertaken by hand. Fortunately, there is now available a wide range of programs to do this assessment quickly. Not only do such programs permit rapid determination of the rate of return under the basic set of economic and operating conditions, but they also allow an equally quick analysis of the effects of changing these conditions on the objective function. This worthwhile technique is known as 'sensitivity analysis'.

The capital cost of the proposed project is a vital and major input to the evaluation process, but by no means the only one. The time schedule of expenditures and revenue receipts, and the financial structure of the project (proportion of equity and consequent loan requirement, plus interest rate on the loan and its repayment period) are equally important.

The total investment in the project — that is, the sum of all the money spent up to the day that revenue begins to be earned — may be significantly greater than the capital cost. Working capital and the interest accrued on the building loan during construction have to be calculated, and can represent a large proportion of this additional cost. There are thus three stages in determining the full cost of the project:

(a) plant and equipment cost, including the costs of direct engineering, procurement and delivery to site;

(b) total erected and installed cost (TEC) which is the cost of the complete plant erected and ready to operate, including constructional engineering, labour and materials, all services, buildings and so on;

(c) total capital employed (TCE), which also includes the working capital and financing charges.

Although not a cash item, plant depreciation is an important part of the profit and loss calculation. Depreciation represents the diminishing value of the fixed assets employed by the enterprise through use, the passage of time and obsolescence. Thus, a realistic determination of profit or loss requires some estimate of the rate of depreciation in plant value, often expressed as a fixed percentage (although various other methods exist). Depreciation is normally an allowable deduction from profits before tax, from which the ultimate 'post tax' profits are determined.

The main elements that have to be considered in the financial appraisal are:

- type of project, whether it is batch or continuously operated, and whether one, two or three shifts are needed;
- production rate (or feed rate and yield);
- total installed cost, divided into categories so that the depreciation may be calculated (usually at different rates for buildings, fixed equipment and mobile equipment);
- amount of money available from the project's owners or other investors (the equity);
- means of providing the balance of the TCE — as one loan, or several;
- rates of interest payable on the loan, and the required repayment periods and when they start (usually not until part way through the first year of operation, after revenue has started to be received);
- any fees for loan arrangement or other fixed financing charges;
- an allowance for reduced rates of production in the first year or two of operation;
- length of construction period, which affects the amount of interest accruing during this period;
- an estimate of cash-in-hand, the contingency fund for the first year or so of operation;

- process operating costs, directly proportional to output, such as feedstock, fuel and power, water and waste treatment, chemicals and catalysts, packaging and distribution;
- costs of the work force — salaries and directly-related overhead costs (pensions, payroll taxes, meals, transport and so on);
- general overheads — the costs of administration and marketing;
- working capital requirements, which are needed to pay for feedstock, material in process in the plant, finished product not yet shipped, and product sold but not yet paid for, up to the point of first receipt of sales revenue;
- an allowance for other pre-production expenditures (such as recruitment and training of plant personnel);
- rate of taxation on profits and the impact of any development area assistance (such as any tax 'holiday' or investment grants or subsidies);
- rates of inflation to be applied to the variable costs (which increase with time, whereas the capital costs do not).

It is normal in a calculation of this kind to subtract the annual operating costs from the anticipated sales revenue for each year of operation, and to use this net revenue as the 'income' side of the analysis. Investment can thus be regarded as complete by the commencement of operation, and this is usually the point at which the analysis is done — discounting all investment forward to this time, and all income back to it.

2.6 Project implementation

As has been indicated above, once a decision has been taken to proceed and funds have been approved, the control of the project is usually vested in a project manager (or project engineer) who coordinates the many different activities, with often conflicting priorities, to ensure that an efficient and safe plant is handed over for production, on time and within the funds allocated. The framework for detailed design, cost control and planning is established at this time[3].

One of the earliest decisions to be taken is which type of contractual arrangement needs to be adopted. Although many variations are possible, construction contracts are essentially of two kinds: lump-sum[4] or cost-reimbursable[5].

Lump-sum contracts are sought when most of the main design work has been completed before the contractors are invited to tender for the work on a competitive basis for completion by a specified date. The contract price includes not only the direct cost of the works, but also that of any outstanding detailed design, overheads and profit, and a provision for the contractor's risk involved. Provision is made for price adjustments arising from variations or other factors outside the contractor's control via a contract price adjustment (CPA) clause written into the conditions of contract together with agreed formulae.

A lump-sum contract based on full design generally leads to the best defined programme and lowest direct cost. However, the time required for this approach is often unacceptable, particularly for major capital projects, and in uncertain economic conditions few contractors would wish to accept business on such terms.

Cost-reimbursable contracts are appropriate when a contractor is appointed before design work is complete and when, therefore, a final cost of the work cannot be established with any accuracy. With contracts of this type, it is usual for part of the cost to be on a fixed fee or percentage-of-works basis, with all the remaining costs incurred by the contractor directly reimbursed by the client. When negotiating a contract of this type, the main elements to be considered are any or all of the following:

- profit and overheads;
- design;
- project management;
- procurement and inspection;
- site supervision;
- equipment supply;
- construction and erection;
- commissioning.

A negotiated contract of the cost-reimbursable type is often adopted for process plants to obtain the greater flexibility — for example, to accept design or specification changes — offered by it and yet achieve the shortest overall time to the commissioning of the new facilities. At a time of rapidly-changing costs, this type of contract has the further advantage that the tenderer does not need to guess at the likely effect of time on costs, as done when bidding on a lump-sum basis. (These contracts are more costly and difficult to administer and are therefore sometimes converted to lump-sum contracts when risks have been reduced during the course of the project.)

The choice of contract type and the negotiation with (and final selection of) a contractor require the application of considerable experience and judgement, the discussion of which is outside the scope of this book: but useful information can be found in IChemE's *An Engineer's Guide to the Model Forms of Conditions of Contract*[6].

In the case of a cost-reimbursable type contract, construction on site commences at a stage when design is sufficiently advanced to ensure that construction work can proceed smoothly and efficiently to completion. As the site establishment costs (supervision, clerical, hutting and so on) are a significant proportion of the total cost of the work and are incurred irrespective of work load on site, close control of design and procurement is necessary to avoid partial suspension of site work arising from design changes, late information, late deliveries and similar causes. For this reason, the pressure to open up a site early to demonstrate activity to management must be resisted. It should be recognized that gearing design and procurement to a progressive pattern will somewhat increase the cost of these activities to achieve the overall benefit of a shorter project time. The natural inclination of design engineers to seek improvements must be recognized and controlled, if the programme is not to be put at risk.

With lump-sum contracts, control of all the features listed above is essential to ensure that the project proceeds on time and within budget and that no 'surprises' arise. In this case, the detailed monitoring of costs is carried out within the contractor's organization but the client must still exercise effective management control of the time taken in making decisions, the authorization of changes and the detailed design and progress of work.

When developing the construction programme, the possibility of achieving earlier completion by accelerating certain activities (at increased total project cost such as overtime working) may need to be evaluated against the total financial benefit to the company arising from the earlier production. If this course is adopted, particularly in respect of early activities on site, there must be reasonable assurance that any time advantage gained will not be lost by slippage of later work.

Delays at the commissioning stage are not only amongst the most frequently encountered but are also the most expensive as, by this time, most of the funds have been expended, operating personnel engaged and process materials employed. Considerable effort to minimize these delays is therefore justified and includes the following (in addition to adequate development, design work and operability studies):

- provision of additional instrumentation, sampling points and means of withdrawing or recycling streams in the event of failure of certain items to perform to specification;
- early proving of components and circuits under simulated conditions to identify any shortfalls in performance and operating problems, leaving sufficient time for their rectification if required;

- adequate provision of construction materials, fittings, operating spares, instruments and some equipment items additional to those required to construct the plant as designed. Although increasing the apparent project cost, they enable modifications to be carried out promptly and if not required will become the basis of the operating plant's maintenance stock.

In order to ensure a smooth transfer from construction, through commissioning to routine operation, adequate consultation and training of personnel must be arranged within the project implementation period.

Consultation includes safety reviews to identify, for instance, necessary additional safeguarding control devices, possible abnormal service conditions to which equipment or fittings may be subjected, emission or noise control, or the need for modifications to increase the safety of operating procedures. Reviews with maintenance engineers may indicate design changes desirable to reduce downtime and cost during the service life of the plant. Where appropriate, consultation with Trade Union and Safety and Welfare Committee representatives must also be given timely consideration.

Training programmes ensure that operators, safety crews and maintenance personnel are familiar with operating procedures, special process and plant features and control systems, as well as with the layout of the plant and its operating points, before commissioning begins.

The engineer must ensure that these activities take place at agreed stages in the project development and would be well advised to allow some further time and resources for dealing with items arising from discussion of these matters. Unless these aspects are given adequate and timely attention during the project implementation stage, significant delays and additional expenditure are likely to incur during commissioning and start-up of the plant.

References in Chapter 2

1. Lawson, G., Wearne, S. and Iles-Smith, P., 1999, *Project Management for the Process Industries* (IChemE, UK).
2. Allen, D., 1991, *Economic Evaluation of Projects* (IChemE, UK).
3. Kharbanda, O.P. and Stallworthy, E.A., 1985, *Effective Project Cost Control* (IChemE, UK).
4. IChemE, 1995, *Model Form of Conditions of Contract for Process Plant — Lump-sum Contracts*, 'The Red Book', 3rd edn (IChemE, UK).
5. IChemE, 1992, *Model Form of Conditions of Contract for Process Plant — Reimbursable Contracts,* 'The Green Book', 2nd edn (IChemE, UK).
6. Wright, D., 1998, *An Engineer's Guide to the IChemE Model Forms of Conditions of Contract*, 'The Purple Book', 3rd edn (IChemE, UK).

Cost estimation and project development

3

3.1 Introduction

At an early stage after the conception of a new process route or when a new or extended production facility is contemplated, the experienced engineer prepares a quick appraisal of costs. If the project goes beyond this early stage, then the cost appraisal will be an iterative process, culminating in a detailed listing of estimated costs against which actual project costs can be monitored.

The purpose of this chapter is to set out a typical scheme describing and defining stages of development of a cost estimate by considering:

- stage of project development and data which are available when the estimate is prepared;
- summary of techniques used in preparing the cost estimate;
- approximate cost of preparing the estimate;
- probable magnitude of error in the estimate;
- purpose for which the estimate is generally suitable.

Commonly-used synonyms applied to each estimating stage have also been listed but great caution must be exercised before accepting the equivalence of any terminology until the basis on which a particular estimate was prepared and its purpose has been established.

Only rarely will all the stages of estimating, described below, be followed in the development of a particular project. Sometimes a large return on capital is foreseen, subject to a rapid entry into the market. It may then be decided to accept a more hurried estimate having wider tolerance and to enter into the engineering phase, including ordering of long delivery items and site preparation works. In such cases, it is usual for a detailed estimate to be built up in stages as soon as practicable. Again, in the case of a company (either owner or contractor) involved in a repetition of a very similar, recently constructed unit, estimates within ±10% and often within ±5% can be prepared rapidly whilst avoiding much of the preliminary work and associated cost. However, there is generally some progression from initial estimating, based on limited information, to a more detailed estimate as the project is more fully defined: the stages of estimate development described provide a guide to the type of estimate in relation to the level of information available.

3.2 Types and classification of estimates

Even today, the terminology and classification of estimates are still not universally standardized despite efforts to overcome this problem. In 1958, the American Association of Cost Engineers published five definitions of estimate types as follows:

- order of magnitude (variable accuracy over ±30%);
- study estimate (factored estimate, accuracy up to ±30%);
- preliminary estimate (generally for authorization, accuracy ±20%);
- definitive estimate (more detailed information, accuracy ±10%);
- detailed estimate (contractor's estimate, accuracy ±5%).

3.2.1 Order of magnitude estimate

(Also known as the ratio, seat-of-the-pants, guesstimate, or ballpark estimate.)

An approximate forecast of fixed investment may be obtained without flowsheet, layout or equipment analysis by applying overall ratios (to account for differences in scale of production) and appropriate escalation factors to update from previous installations considered to be broadly similar in nature to the scheme under consideration. Illustration of the use of exponential cost estimating techniques is given in Section 4.4.3, page 32.

If there is not an adequate precedent, then an outline flowsheet is necessary to identify the main processing steps and flow quantities. Given this information, one or more of the step counting methods (see Section 4.3) can be used to estimate capital costs. It is advisable to apply more than one of these methods in order to form some measure of confidence in the estimate.

Relatively little effort is expended carrying out this type of estimate which will be used only as a very coarse screen to gauge the degree of further interest. The probable error range will be within ±30% to ±50%; but some authorities will say that no confidence level can reasonably be applied to such estimates! (It is worth pointing out here that whilst it is conventional to talk about ±x% accuracy figures, in reality an under-estimate is limited by the −100% figure, whereas an over-estimate is theoretically unlimited.)

3.2.2 Study estimate

(Also known as the evaluation or predesign estimate.)

When a scheme has been developed to the stage of preliminary flowsheets, with the duty rating of principal items of equipment specified and a geographical location for the construction of the facility known, it is feasible to prepare a cost estimate based upon estimates for each main plant item or group of items. These are obtained by applying appropriate exponents to previously established plant costs to account for differences in duty rating or size and to incorporate electrical, instrument, piping, civil and structural work. An example of exponent estimating applied to elements of a process plant project is set out in Section 4.4.4. The cost of getting this estimate is likely to be between 0.1 and 0.2% of the total project cost with a probable order of error within ±20% to ±30% (see Table 3.1).

It is usual for the degree of interest in the project to be reviewed at this stage. All the principal factors affecting a decision to proceed beyond this stage are reassessed. There may be a hold placed on progress due to failure to identify a suitable site or source of raw materials; or possibly further laboratory results are required. If, as a result of the review, a decision is made to proceed further with the project, then a marked increase in the rate and amount of expenditure on engineering and associated activities will result. This effort will yield, as one of its results, a much more detailed and accurate estimate upon which the important decision to sanction funds will depend.

Table 3.1 Probable accuracy against the cost of the estimate

Recommended nomenclature	Probable range of accuracy	Cost as % of project expenditure
Detailed estimate	±2 to ±5%	5 to 10%
Definitive estimate	±5 to 15%	1 to 3%
Preliminary estimate	±10 to 25%	0.4 to 0.8%
Study estimate	±20 to ±30%	0.1 to 0.2%
Order of magnitude estimate	±30 to ±50%	0 to 0.1%

3.2.3 Preliminary estimate

(Also known as the sanction, funding or authorization estimate.)

Following acceptance of a study estimate, the further engineering work, which has been authorized, aims to obtain and present the following information: preliminary material and energy balances, piping and instrument diagrams (P&IDs), equipment lists and material specifications, duty rating and sizing of all process equipment, instrumentation and control devices:

- a basic site layout of main plant blocks, roads, railways, support buildings and a site survey;
- preliminary general arrangement of plant;
- buildings approximately sized and form of construction stated including outline architectural sketches and main structural frame diagrams;
- piping and insulation standards based on preliminary flowsheets;
- preliminary utilities diagrams;
- preliminary electrical single line diagram, motor list, substation list and lighting specification and scheme;
- programme of work to achieve a stated date for production;
- engineering man-hour forecast to complete the project.

With such data available, a cost estimate having a probable error of less than ±20% may be achieved. If the data is too 'preliminary' and incomplete then the probable estimating error may be no better than 25%. Effort must be made to get the project defined and, if this is successful, then estimates in the range ±10% to ±15% may be achieved at this stage, particularly when the major plant items are accurately assessed.

For several items such as pipework, insulation, electrical and instrumentation work, estimates are derived by applying factors to the estimated costs of main items of equipment. Specifying the principal materials of construction will aid in selecting the appropriate factor for piping cost. Again, the electric motor list and preliminary total of installed power enables the nature of electrical work to be forecast more clearly and the appropriate cost factor selected. But much of the estimate is determined by considering the cost of individual items, small groups of equipment, structures and buildings. The cost estimate, which has now considered almost all major equipment on an individual basis, is related to a quantitative and qualitative description of the equipment. The factorial estimating method is discussed further in Section 4.5.

The cost of the effort so far expended will typically total between 0.4% and 0.8% of project final cost; but for this expenditure a comprehensive statement of forecast cost to carry out the project will be available. This cost estimate forms part of a report to management on all aspects of the intended project including the benefits which are anticipated to arise from the investment and, most importantly, the assumptions on which the report is founded. It is on the basis of this type of report that approval should be sought from management to proceed.

All subsequent actions and decisions should be compared to this source document; all proposals to change from the original plan in terms of money, time or method should be analysed by reference to the original intentions.

3.2.4 Definitive estimate

(Also known as the control estimate.)

Following the authorization to proceed and the allocation of project funds based upon the preliminary stage estimate, it is usual to further define and refine estimates as design work proceeds and decisions are made. At a point short of complete drawings and specifications but with the benefit of substantial detail being known and having held discussions with vendors and, when appropriate, with engineering and erection contractors, the manager of the project will require a definitive estimate to be drawn up. Although estimating error can range up to ±15%, this estimate will normally aim for a probable error in the range ±5% to ±10% and will be a key cost control document used by the project manager to monitor all future expenditure against the authorized funds. By the time this project control estimate is prepared, between 1% and 3% of the final project cost is likely to have been spent on this activity.

3.2.5 Detailed estimate

(Also known as the tender or contractor's final cost estimate.)

This estimate is prepared when a considerable amount of engineering design work has been completed, bills of quantities and material take-offs carried out and, unfortunately, it is a costly exercise. Process and mechanical datasheets are prepared and vendors' quotations for selected items of equipment obtained so that competitive prices compatible with quality and delivery are available for the estimate. In the case of a contractor, there will be a firm commitment to the client and a high degree of accuracy is therefore required. The key is the equipment list should be structured in 'shopping list' form enabling costs to be allocated to each item. A reasonable plant layout must be developed to enable the bulk items, such as electrics, instruments, piping and valves, structures, civil works and buildings to be quantified and taken off. All other costs (see Appendix to Chapter 5, page 62) such as engineering, management, overheads, construction, and so on must be added to arrive at a total project capital cost. The probable order of error-will be ±2% to ±5% for an estimate prepared in this way and its cost could be upwards of 5% of total project costs, especially if most of the essential engineering has been completed.

3.3 The cost of cost estimates

The greater the size of project under consideration, the cost of preparing an estimate (at any desired level of accuracy) tends to decrease as a percentage of project total cost.

Broadly speaking, extended project study periods, frequent changes of scope of work, uncertainty of basic data, development into new areas of technology for the organization, or inadequate management associated with the project, will often result in the cost of preparing an estimate exceeding the bands given in Table 3.1, but repetitive project work will enable estimates to be prepared at costs less than the lower figure. As always, the law of diminishing returns applies here, so extra estimating and design work do not always result in greater accuracy! Clearly, the cost of preparing cost estimates is dependent not only on the nature and scale of the project but also on the experience, sophistication and overhead structure of the organization preparing the estimate.

Table 3.1 gives a summary of the expected accuracy ranges and approximate costs of the preparation of estimates for the various estimate classifications described in this chapter.

Estimating methods

4

4.1 Introduction

As explained in Chapter 3, the purpose and timing of a capital estimate determines the type of estimate methodology which is appropriate to the purpose. On the other hand, the information available determines the accuracy that is possible and the type of estimate that is feasible. It is costly and wasteful to produce a better estimate than is required, but misleading to produce an estimate that purports to be better than can be justified by the data available.

In principle, the group of estimating methods described in this chapter cover estimating requirements from early research to contracts — that is, order of magnitude through to detailed estimates.

If a project involves a new process, it is necessary to obtain cost estimates early in the research, in order to decide if the project is viable. Furthermore, if expensive processing routes are identified, it may be possible to direct research towards objectives that will yield a more economic process. Cost estimating methods are available for these purposes. These methods are based on firstly recognizing the essential processing steps within a process and then estimating their cost using published correlations. These 'step counting' methods require only a simple quantities flow sheet plus approximate information about operating conditions. They do not need any engineering data except for an indication of the probable materials of construction.

When a project is based on modifying a previous design, a lot of data will be available from earlier projects, including cost information. If the project involves an identical process, but at a different scale, an initial cost estimate can be made on the basis that the total plant cost is related to plant capacity raised to a power. A better estimate is possible if the total plant cost can be broken down into broad categories (such as main plant items, piping, structures and so on) and the 'exponential' method applied to each category, separately, using a different exponent for each. The total plant cost is then the sum of the costs of all the separate categories.

The methods described so far do not require any detailed knowledge of the equipment that will be employed. Very early on in the process design it is possible to specify the approximate size, and therefore the approximate purchase price, of all the main items of equipment. The total cost of purchasing the main items can be converted to a total erected cost (TEC) if it is multiplied by an overall installation factor known to be typical of the type of process. A better estimate is possible if the purchased cost of each item is converted, separately, to an erected cost using an installation factor known to be typical of that type of item; the total erected cost is then the sum of all the separate erected costs. This factorial or modular method can be extended by dividing the installation factor for each item of equipment into sub-factors that represent the different engineering activities which go into the erection of each item.

As a project progresses, more and more information is generated and it becomes possible to prepare a detailed 'shopping list' for all the components and labour that will be needed. This information forms the basis for a detailed estimate.

4.2 Common principles

Four different methods are described and illustrated: step counting, power law or exponential, factorial and detailed methods.

Many versions of these methods are in use, but all are based on an analysis of historical cost data. This analysis requires the data to be broken down into the categories mentioned above, according to fairly arbitrary conventions, and correlated. Therefore, it is necessary to be consistent when using the correlations in order to avoid omissions, duplications or inaccuracies.

As most cost data is historical it may not be exactly suitable to the purpose in hand and it may also be erroneous; thus the estimated cost of a single item may be significantly in error. The importance of this depends on circumstances:

- if the total cost of a plant is estimated by treating the plant as a single item, then its cost may be seriously in error unless the input data is exceptionally good;
- if a total plant cost is estimated from the sum of many component costs it can be shown that the variance of the total is smaller than the variance of the separate components. All the better cost estimating methods rely for their potential accuracy on a multiplicity of such sub-estimates with errors tending to cancel out, rather than being magnified. It is essential that the sub-estimates do not contain any systematic errors.

However, even the best methods cannot compensate for the omission or duplication of significant cost items.

4.3 Step count estimating

This approach to obtaining an order-of-magnitude capital cost estimate is based on establishing a model which relates basic process parameters, such as capacity or throughput, temperature, pressure and materials of construction, to total erected cost and taking into account either the number of main plant items or the number of functional units involved.

4.3.1 Step count estimating – main plant item basis

One relatively simple approach was derived by Wilson[1] who proposed the following correlation for 1971:

$$C = f N \, (AUC) \, F_M F_P F_T$$

where,

C — capital cost of plant, £, in 1971;

f — investment factor (q.v. Lang factor) depends on dominant phase and AUC, and is obtained graphically (see Figure 4.1, overleaf);

N — number of all main plant items except pumps;

AUC — average unit cost of main plant items $= 21V^{0.675}$ (where V is the average capacity in the original work, but works well when plant output, tons per year, is used);

F_M — factor for materials of construction which ranges from 1.0 for mild steel to 2.0 for titanium (see Table 4.1, page 23). A weighted mean value may be used;

F_P — factor for design pressure, which is applicable only outside the range 1–7 bar, and is obtained graphically (see Figure 4.2, page 23);

F_T — factor for design temperature outside the range 0 to 100°C and is obtained graphically (see Figure 4.3, page 23).

An adjusted UK plant cost index (see Chapter 8) also needs to be included for current costs, which gives the following expression for 2000:

$$£_{2000} \, C = 20.75 \, f N \, (AUC) \, F_M F_P F_T$$

The validity of updating over such long time periods is discussed later in Chapter 8.

As the correlation was derived from a study of only 16 processes and an accuracy of ±30% claimed for only 13 of them, the method might be considered to have a low level of credibility. In practice, cost estimates from this procedure generally seem to come out quite well. The method is simple to use and only requires the total number of main plant items in the process. For order-of-magnitude estimating, however, even this level of information requirement may not be available.

The same principle and approach was adopted by Allen and Page[2], but their model is more sophisticated and requires more information.

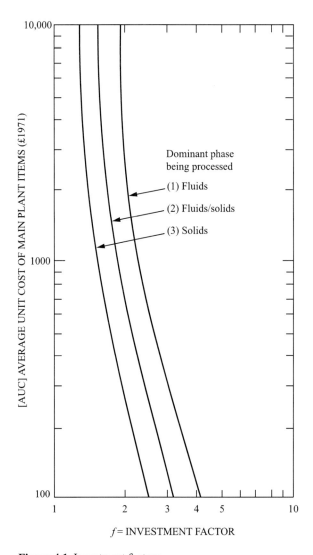

Figure 4.1 Investment factors

Table 4.1 Materials of construction factors

1.0	Mild steel	1.55	Hastelloy C
1.07	Aluminium and bronze	1.65	Monel
1.1	Cast steel	1.7	Nickel and iconel
1.3	Stainless steel	2.0	Titanium
1.5	Higher grades of stainless steel		

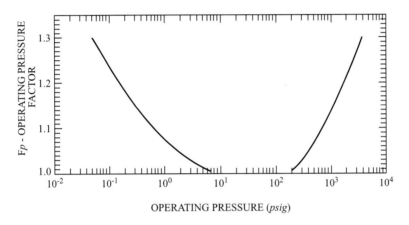

Figure 4.2 Pressure factor

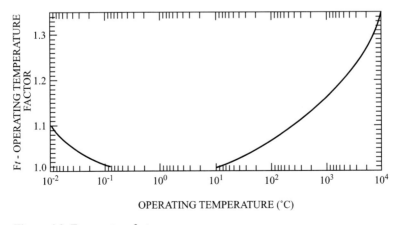

Figure 4.3 Temperature factor

4.3.2 Step count estimating – functional unit basis

The concept of 'number of steps' in a process influencing costs was first suggested by Wessel[3] in proposing a correlation for labour costs. Later, Hill[4] assigned costs to 'standard units', which is seen as the precursor of the functional units employed by Zevnik and Buchanan[5], and in methods described in this book and the 'process steps' approach used by Taylor[6].

A *functional unit* is a significant step in a chemical process which includes all equipment fully installed and ready for that step to operate. A more detailed explanation and definition is given in Table 4.2 which encompasses all development work on this principle of estimating, except for Taylor who defines his steps by example.

To illustrate the concept of a functional unit an outline flowsheet for an acetic anhydride process is shown in Figure 4.4. The five functional units of this process, each encompassing all equipment and ancillaries for operation of that unit, are clearly identified and may be compared with the detailed flowsheet of the same process shown in Figure 4.5, which incorporates 26 main plant items. The costing of this process by each of the step counting methods described in this section is set out in the appendix, page 51.

Table 4.2 Explanation and definition of a functional unit

- A functional unit is a significant step in a process and includes all equipment and ancillaries necessary for operation of that unit. Thus, the sum of the costs of all functional units in a process gives the total capital cost.

- Generally, a functional unit may be characterized as a unit operation, unit process, or separation method that has energy transfer, moving parts and/or a high level of 'internals'.

- Pumping and heat exchange are ignored as they are considered as part of a functional unit unless substantial special loads such as refrigeration are involved.

- Storage 'in process' is ignored, unless mechanical handling is involved — that is, for solids — as the cost of storage is relatively low and tends to be a constant function of the process. Large storages of raw materials, intermediates or products are usually treated separately from 'the process' in the estimate.

- Multi-stream operation is taken as one unit.

- Simple 'mechanical' separation where there are no moving parts is ignored — that is, cyclone, gravity settler — as the cost is usually relatively insignificant.

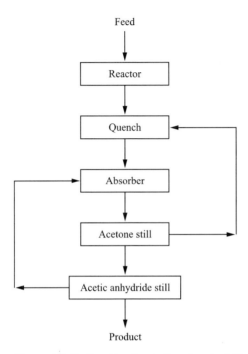

Figure 4.4 Outline flowsheet of acetic anhydride process

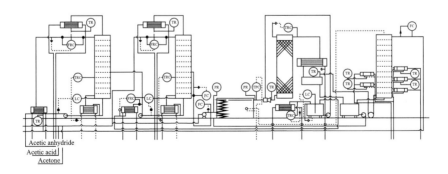

Figure 4.5 Detailed flowsheet of acetic anhydride process

25

The principle of the step count functional unit estimating method is that the average cost of a functional unit in a process is a function of various process parameters:

Capital cost per functional unit $= f(Q,T,P,M)$

where,
Q — capacity or throughput;
T — temperature;
P — pressure;
M — material of construction.

Although there may be major differences between different units, for example, a distillation unit and a compressor, these differences are averaged out over the process as a whole. The advantages and justification for the approach are:

- with the information available at this stage of estimating, there is no indication of relative costs of different items;
- the costs of the items in any case are immaterial as it is the overall capital cost being estimated;
- justification may be claimed on grounds of equiprobability;
- it appears to work for the preparation of order-of-magnitude estimates.

The concept is now widely accepted as a valid preliminary estimating procedure by many international companies.

Zevnik and Buchanan's method[5]

One of the earliest applications of the functional unit method of capital cost estimation was due to Zevnik and Buchanan. They developed an essentially graphical technique for obtaining the cost of one functional unit based on plant capacity, maximum pressure, maximum temperature and materials of construction. This cost per functional unit (CPF) is then multiplied by the number of functional units, a utilities factor of 1.33 and a cost index based on the Engineering News Record (ENR) construction cost index.

The CPF is read from a graph of CPF versus plant capacity for a range of complexity factors (CF) calculated from the following expression:

$$CF = 2 \times 10^{(F_t + F_p + F_m)}$$

where,
F_t — temperature factor, read from a graph of F_t versus maximum (or minimum) process temperature;

F_p — pressure factor, read from a graph of F_p versus maximum (or minimum) process pressure;

F_m — materials of construction factor read from a table of factors from 0 for mild steel and wood to 0.4 for precious metals.

The overall procedure can be expressed as a series of equations depending on plant capacity, temperature, pressure, and number of functional units. The original work has been updated to 2000 with an adjusted ENR construction cost index (see Chapter 8). While this index is inappropriate for process plant, comprising costs of steel, cement and building construction labour, it was used in the original work, so it is retained here. Currency conversion is at $2/£ (relevant at the time of the original work) to account for exchange rate and location effects where the validity of which is discussed in Chapter 8. This gives the following equations (a) to (d). All correlations are for gas phase processes, inside battery limits.

(a) For plant capacity above 10 million lb/year (4536 tonnes/y) and temperature and pressure above ambient:

$$C = 7470 N Q^{0.6} \ 10^{[(0.1 \log P_{max}) + (1.8 \times 10^{-4} (T_{max} - 300)) + (F_m)]}$$

where,

C — estimated capital cost, £ million, 2000;

Q — plant capacity, tons per year;

N — number of functional units;

P_{max} — maximum process pressure (atmospheres);

T_{max} — maximum process temperature, K;

F_m — materials of construction factor:

  0 for mild steel and wood;

  0.1 for aluminium, brass, lower grade stainless steel;

  0.2 for monel, nickel, higher grade stainless steel;

  0.3 for hastelloy;

  0.4 for precious metals.

(b) For plant capacities below 10 million lb/year (4536 tonnes/y), the equation becomes:

$$C = 17,280 N Q^{0.5} \ 10^{[(0.1 \log P_{max}) + (1.8 \times 10-4 \, T_{max} - 300)) + (F_m)]}$$

(c) For subambient temperatures, the temperature factor becomes:

$$(0.57 - (1.9 \times 10^{-2} \, T_{min})) \text{ in place of } (1.8 \times 10^{-4} (T_{max} - 300))$$

(d) For subambient pressures, the pressure factor becomes:

$0.1 \log \left(\dfrac{1}{P_{min}} \right)$ in place of $(0.1 \log (P_{max}))$

Zevnik and Buchanan's definition of a functional unit 'refers to all equipment necessary to carry out a single significant process function'. There were difficulties in applying this definition which is evident from the inconsistencies in the worked examples, and the authors confessed to an 'unconscious bias'. There were also problems both in the reliability of published data and also in the boundaries of plant under consideration – whether a battery limits cost or greenfield site cost was being derived.

Taylor's method[6]

This procedure has been developed from internal ICI estimating methods and is based on real costs — that is, the cost of actual plants built by ICI over a 10-year period from 1963–74. The 'process steps' are effectively 'functional units', although reference should be made to the published list for accuracy. The basic procedure is represented by:

$C = K\, C_i\, (Q)^s$

where,

C — capital cost;
K — constant;
C_i — costliness index = $\overset{N}{\underset{1}{}}\ (1.3)^y$;
Q — capacity;
s — scale factor;
N — number of process steps (see paper for definition and explanation);
y — 'complexity score' which is developed by constructing a table in which each functional unit is scored '0', '1', '2' or '3' for each of eight features, the scoring being a crude measure of the extent to which a 'real' plant departs from a 'standard' plant by not being made of carbon steel, not operating at ambient temperature and pressure and incorporates multistreams (see appendix, page 51, for a worked example).

For 2000, UK, battery limit, conditions:

$£C = 379{,}700\ C_i\, Q^{0.39}$

where,

Q — capacity in 000s tonnes/y;
C_i — costliness index.

Timms' method[7]

A much simpler approach for gas phase processes only, including both organic and inorganic chemical products, uses the following equations which have been derived from the original work by updating with an adjusted US plant cost index (see Chapter 8) and converting at $2/£ to account for exchange rate and location effects.

(a) Simple equation:

$$C = 10560 \, N Q^{0.615}$$

(b) With materials of construction, temperature and pressure effects:

$$C = 4910 \, N Q^{0.639} \, F_m \, (T_{max})^{0.066} \, (P_{max})^{-0.016}$$

where,

C — capital cost in UK £$_{2000}$, battery limits;
N — number of functional units;
Q — plant capacity, t/y;
F_m — materials of construction factor:
   1.0 for carbon steel;
   1.15 for low grade stainless steel;
   1.2 for medium grade stainless steel;
   1.3 for high grade stainless steel:
T_{max} — maximum process temperature, K;
P_{max} — maximum process pressure, bars.

Bridgwater's method[8]

For processes with predominantly liquid and/or solid handling phases, there is the following equation:

(a) Plant capacities above 60,000 tonne/y:

$$C = 1930 \, N \left(\frac{Q}{s} \right)^{0.675}$$

where,

C — capital cost, £$_{2000}$, battery limits;
N — number of functional units;
Q — plant capacity, tonne/y, above 60,000;
s — reactor 'conversion';
(thus Q/s represents process throughput, tonnes/y).

(b) Plant capacities below 60,000 tonne/y:

$$C = 169,560 \, N \left(\frac{Q}{s}\right)^{0.30}$$

General approach

The principle that capital cost is a function of a number of steps and basic process parameters, particularly capacity or throughput, can be applied to any special situation to derive a model for that industry or group of processes.

Two examples of specific correlations are:

(a) Refuse sorting and separation processes:

$$C = 3250 \, N \, (686 + Q)$$

C — capital cost, £$_{2000}$, battery limits basis;
N — number of functional units;
Q — plant capacity in tonnes refuse feed per day;

(b) Non-biological effluent treatment:

$$C = 1900 \, Ne \, Q^{0.453}$$

where,

C — capital cost, £$_{2000}$, battery limits basis, fully automated plant. Buildings not included;
Q — design throughput, imperial gallons per hour;
Ne — number of effluent treatment steps. Effluent treatment steps are:
- acid/alkali neutralization;
- chrome reduction, aqueous (if gaseous sulphur dioxide is used, add a further half step);
- cyanide oxidations to cyanate, aqueous (if gaseous chlorine used add a further half step);
- demulsification;
- filter press;
- ion exchange;
- lime reagent preparation;
- settlement;
- water recycle system.

In SI units, the correlation is:

$$C = \; 1750 \, Ne \, Q^{0.453}$$

where,

Q — throughput, m^3h^{-1}.

The capital cost includes all equipment, materials, labour, civils installation, commissioning and cubicle for the control panel. Reagent warehousing would cost about 20% more, and complete enclosure up to 100% more.

The purpose of these examples is to show how easy it is for a user to collect cost data and generate a relationship for the type of process of interest. This often gives a more reliable answer than the standard correlations given earlier.

4.4 Power law or exponential estimating

4.4.1 Applications

Power law or exponential methods permit cost estimates to be made rapidly by extrapolating cost data from one scale to another. Thus the total cost of a proposed plant can be derived from historical cost data by using:

- the total cost of a similar (reference) plant;
- a comparatively simple breakdown of the costs of a similar plant;
- costs for parts of related plants that can be assembled to represent the proposed plant.

A cost index is always needed to give a current cost. The exponential method is also an important aid in deriving the cost of main plant items (MPI). These costs are the starting point of the factorial methods which are discussed later.

4.4.2 Basis

The cost of a specific item — for example, pump, column, piping, complete plant or unit operation/process — depends on size or scale and can often be correlated by the approximate relationship:

$$\frac{C}{C_r} = \left(\frac{S}{S_r}\right)^n$$

or

$$C = k\,S^n$$

where,

C — cost of the item at size or scale S;

C_r — cost of the reference item at size or scale S_r;

n — scale exponent;

k — a constant equalling the nominal cost of the item at unit size or scale.

The dimensions of S — for example, m, m^2, m^3, m^3hr^{-1}, tonne/y, cfm, kW — must be chosen to suit the type of item. The value of k and n depend upon the type of item and the characteristic dimension used; they can be derived from historical costs. Any correlation of this sort will be applicable only over a limited range of size, and the data is often presented as lines on log-log graphs — for examples, see Chapter 7.

Scale exponents n are usually between 0.3 and 1.0, typically 0.6; for this reason the exponential method is often dubbed the '6/10 rule'. In general, exponents depend on the phase that is being processed and n increases along the sequence gas phase, liquid phase and solid phase.

Cost correlations are published for various items of equipment and so on but preferably they should be built up within a company, from data for items in regular use.

Historical costs must be updated to the date of the estimate using appropriate cost indices (see Chapter 8). However, *overall plant costs* that are more than five years old should be escalated with extreme caution and as a last resort because of changes in the scope of the plant due to legislative effects and so on. It is worth pointing out that *equipment costs* and often *unit operation costs* can be updated with a cost index over longer periods than the five years just mentioned.

4.4.3 Estimation of total plant cost – overall basis

The total cost of a proposed plant C can be estimated from the total cost of a similar reference plant C_r again using:

$$\frac{C}{C_r} = \left(\frac{S}{S_r}\right)^n$$

where C is now the *plant* cost and S the *plant* size.

The scale exponent n can be derived from historical data for similar plants. For whole plants, n is usually in the range 0.4 to 0.8, typically 0.65. This depends upon the nature of the process and n tends towards 1.0 as process scale increases. This is because, as a process is built at progressively larger capacities, it demands equipment larger than is practically available so the degree of multi-streaming, and therefore n, increases with capacity.

For example, an electrolytic cell hall may require hundreds of cells — that is, it is intrinsically a multi-stream process, so the exponent for a cell hall (including purification) might be about 0.8. With this degree of multi-streaming, there may be significant economies due to the semi-mass production of components.

Clearly, the predicted cost will be on the same basis as the historical costs — for example, if the cost of the reference plant is a *battery limits* cost (see Glossary) then the cost of the proposed plant will also be on a battery limits basis, unless some adjustment is made.

The accuracy of the estimate depends upon the similarity of the proposed and reference plants and also on the validity of the cost index employed. If the two plants are very similar and if their differences are accounted for, the estimate may be accurate to better than ±10%. However, such accuracy is not usual and the method is used only for order of magnitude and study estimates.

The exponential method should not be used to scale a plant capital cost estimate up or down by a factor of more than five, based on capacity. This is because the exponent is itself a function of scale.

Example

The cost is required of a 1500 tonne/day ammonia plant to be erected in the UK on a greenfield site at a specified date. Cost data is available for a plant that is similar in every respect but capacity.

Scope of proposed plant: battery limits process plant; natural gas feedstock. Process units are in a single stream consisting of a reformer furnace; CO conversion; Benfield CO_2 removal; ICI NH_3 synthesis and recovery (single train compressors); boiler feedwater and steam raising, but excluding offsites, storage and auxiliary services.

Cost information: a 1000 tonne/day ammonia plant on the same basis at the same time would cost £65.35 million. The scale exponent is 0.66 for this type of plant.

Cost equation:

$$\frac{C}{C_r} = \left(\frac{S}{S_r} \right)^n$$

thus,

$$C = C_r \left(\frac{S}{S_r} \right)^n$$

where,

C — cost of proposed plant at S tonnes/d;

C_r — cost of known plant at S_r tonnes/d.

Therefore,

$$C = 65.35 \left(\frac{1500}{1000} \right)^{0.66} = £85.4 \text{ million}$$

Battery limits capital cost is estimated to be about £85 million at the time (no allowance needs to be made for inflation because both the reference plant and the proposed plant are costed at the same time).

4.4.4 Estimation of total plant cost – from a simple breakdown based on cost areas

One way to sub-divide total plant cost is as follows:

(a) total equipment — for example, all main items of process equipment;

(b) bulk items — steel structures, piping, electrical, instrumentation, lagging, painting and materials such as catalysts and oils;

(c) civil — for example, roads, drains, foundations, piling and buildings;

(d) construction — for example, labour, sub-contractors, site supervision, tools, hire charges;

(e) engineering and procurement— for example, design and ordering;

(f) office costs — for example, project management, expenses and overheads;

(e) contingencies — an allowance for unlisted items and uncertainty of estimating such as physical items (allowances for political and commercial risks are outside the scope of this book);

(h) inflation and escalation — see Chapter 8.

Given the historical data for plants similar to the proposed plant, it is possible to determine the exponents that correlate each of the above categories and sub-categories, using capacity as a measure of scale. Correlations obtained in this way can be used to build up the cost of the proposed plant at a different scale to that of the original data. The method is illustrated in Table 4.3 using the previous example — that is, an ammonia plant is scaled up from 1000 tonne/day to 1500 tonne/day.

Table 4.3 Exponential cost estimating total plant cost from individual cost sections

Description of cost area	Ammonia plant cost data			
	Item at 1000 tonne/day £million	Scale exponent n	Cost factor 1.5^n	Item at 1500 tonne/day £million
(a) Equipment items				
Furnace heaters and so on	6.63	0.7	1.328	8.80
Package plant	1.07	0.75	1.355	1.45
Heat exchangers	5.91	0.65	1.302	7.69
Compressors and fans	3.13	0.75	1.355	4.24
Pumps	1.07	0.8	1.383	1.48
Turbines	2.35	0.7	1.328	3.12
Tanks	0.14	0.65	1.302	0.18
Vessels and columns	5.20	0.65	1.302	6.77
Miscellaneous items	0.36	0.6	1.275	0.46
Sub-total cost of equipment	25.86	(0.69)	1.322	34.19
(b) Bulk items				
Electrics	2.28	0.7	1.328	3.03
Instrumentation	5.05	0.6	1.275	6.44
Piping	6.40	0.7	1.328	8.50
Structural steel	1.78	0.65	1.302	2.32
Insulation and painting	0.43	0.65	1.302	0.56
Catalysts and chemicals	0.85	1.0	1.500	1.28
Sub-total cost of bulk items	16.79	(0.68)	(1.323)	22.13
(a) Total equipment	25.86	(0.69)	(1.322)	34.19
(b) Total bulk items	16.79	(0.68)	(1.323)	23.13
(c) Civil works	2.21	0.65	1.302	2.88
(d) Construction	11.59	0.65	1.302	15.09
(e) Engineering and procurement fee	6.90	0.5	1.225	8.45
TOTAL COST	63.35	(0.66)	(1.307)	82.74

Battery limits capital cost estimate = £83 million at a given date.

No allowance has been made for owner's home office costs, contingencies or inflation. The items in brackets have been calculated by working backwards from the corresponding sub-totals.

4.4.5 Estimating the cost of main plant items

So far, this discussion has been concerned with scaling the cost of whole plants or groups of equipment and services. In the absence of firm cost data, main plant items (MPIs) can be costed in a similar way, using cost graphs or correlations based on the familiar equation:

$$\frac{C}{C_r} = \left(\frac{S}{S_r}\right)^n$$

or

$$C = k\,S^n$$

The measure of scale S is often referred to as a characteristic dimension — that is, it is a physical quantity characteristic of the equipment in the sense that it correlates well with the cost of the equipment. It is also chosen to correspond with the simple data available at an early stage in design — for example, the cost of pumps can be correlated with fluid flowrate or power consumption. In this case, the values of n and k depend on the characteristic dimension — that is, flowrate or power — and k also depends on the units used such as $m^3 hr^{-1}$ and kW. Chapter 7 has a set of these cost curves for commonly-occuring types of process equipment. If an item is not included in the data set of cost correlations, then contact an equipment vendor if necessary. Alternatively, a rough costing can be obtained on the basis of 'similar' items for which cost data is available, or the weight of the problem item can be estimated and used for guidance as to its approximate cost.

It is important to realize that a cost equation of this sort is a crude approximation to reality and is applicable only over a limited range of scale. Better correlations could be obtained by using two or more variables. However, it is usual to correlate cost using only one variable with the other variables given as qualifying statements. Thus, heat exchanger correlations in terms of area may be restricted to a particular type, material of construction, tube length, working pressure or scale range.

The cost of main plant items relates to specific conditions of supply. These conditions can vary, for example:

- cost, insurance and freight (cif) costs included;
- free on board (fob) — loaded on board ship but subsequent freight and insurance costs excluded, and usually charged to the customer;
- delivered — transportation paid by the supplier;
- incomplete — is some site assembly work required?;
- ex-works — ready to load onto purchaser's transport.

It is important to be sure about these conditions in order to make proper provision for insurance, transportation, tariffs, duties, exchange rates, site costs and so on. It is usual for cost correlations to be given on the basis of the cost of the item delivered to the site, given that they are manufactured in the same country.

As the design progresses, cost data will become available in the form of suppliers' list prices, estimates and quotations thus permitting progressively better cost estimates. Although firm quotations are sound data for immediate purposes, they should not be filed uncritically for future use because current equipment costs depend significantly on the current level of activity in the equipment supplying industry.

Good estimates of total plant cost can be made even though the component equipment costs are up to ±30% in error, providing that many items are being costed — that is, the variance of the total costs is then much less than the variance of its components. Once a total cost has been assembled it should be examined critically and any particularly costly items should be re-costed on a more accurate basis.

4.4.6 General considerations

As the exponential method is an approximation, it can give significant errors if it is used to estimate the cost of a single item. This should be of little importance if the final cost is the sum of many such estimates because, in this case, the errors tend to cancel out. Cancellation is most efficient when there are many sub-estimates, all of roughly equal size and accuracy. This fact should be borne in mind when a historical plant cost is broken down into cost areas for estimating purposes.

It is rare for a new plant to be the same as the previous plant, even if the processes are identical. There are many reasons why this may be so, such as the process conditions may have altered or the required purities changed. If the new plant is built alongside the old plant, it may be able to use some spare capacity such as a surplus reactor or product storage. Site facilities may require almost no additions in order to service the new plant — for example, there may be surplus steam raising or water cooling capacity and it is unlikely that site roads and railways will need changing. Conversely, if the new plant is built on an undeveloped site, it may have to pay heavily for the necessary site services. The cost breakdown must allow these differences to be analysed and accommodated.

It is very important to establish whether a change in capacity is going to be achieved by changing plant dimensions or by changing the number of units, or streams, in parallel. Great care must be taken when scaling upwards or downwards that physical and practical limits are not exceeded — that is, equipment may not be available above or below some limiting size.

4.5 Factorial estimating

4.5.1 Applications

Factorial methods can be used to produce study and preliminary estimates earlier and at far less expense than that incurred for definitive and detailed estimates.

4.5.2 Basis

The methods are based on a historical knowledge of the relative cost of the various purchases and activities that are necessary to build a plant. Table 4.4 shows another example of how total capital employed (TCE) can be broken down into various categories of expenditure and related to purchased equipment cost — the MPI cost. The percentages given were derived for a typical chemical plant installed as an addition to the production of existing products on existing sites. In general, they will depend on several factors, including process type and plant location. For example, the total erected cost for similar plants on undeveloped sites might be twice the numbers indicated. Table 4.4 illustrates the importance of knowing the scope of a quoted capital cost — that is, does it represent total direct plant cost, total capital employed or some intermediate figure?

All factorial methods start by listing and sizing the main plant items. Their purchased cost is then obtained and multiplied by *installation factors* to give a total erected cost. It is obvious that there must be a clear definition of what constitutes a main plant item and in what state it is assumed to be purchased such as complete or incomplete, delivered or awaiting transportation.

Main plant items are usually defined as all the vessels, columns, other fabricated equipment, heat exchangers and machinery that are needed for the project. They are usually costed as if delivered to the site and all the other costs that are necessary to convert them to a working plant must be accounted for by the installation factors.

There are two main sources of error:

• incomplete listing or incorrect costing of the main plant items;
• incorrect installation factors.

Table 4.4 Examples of the composition of total capital investment for process plants

Item	% of delivered equipment cost		
	Solid processing plant*	Solid-fluid processing plant*	Fluid processing plant*
Direct costs			
Purchased equipment delivered (including fabricated equipment and process machinery)	100	100	100
Purchased equipment installation	45	39	47
Instrumentation and controls (installed)	9	13	18
Piping (installed)	16	31	66
Electrical (installed)	10	10	11
Buildings (including services)	25	29	18
Yard improvements	13	10	10
Service facilities (installed)	40	55	70
Land (if purchase is required)	6	6	6
Total direct plant cost	264	293	346
Indirect costs			
Engineering and supervision	33	32	33
Construction expenses	39	34	41
Total direct and indirect plant costs	336	359	420
Contractor's fee (about 5% of direct and indirect plant costs)	17	18	21
Contingency (about 10% of direct and indirect plant costs)	34	36	42
Total erected cost	387	413	483
Working capital (about 15% of total capital investment)	68	74	86
TOTAL CAPITAL EMPLOYED	455	487	569

* A coal briquetting plant would be a typical solid-processing plant

A shale oil plant with crushing, grinding, retorting and extraction would be a typical solid-fluid processing plant

A distillation unit would be a typical fluid-processing plant

(This table is based on Table 17 from Peters, M.S. and Timmerhaus, K.D., 1991, *Plant Design and Economics for Chemical Engineers* (WCB/McGraw-Hill, USA). Reproduced by permission of The McGraw-Hill Companies.)

4.5.3 Total plant cost using an overall installation factor

As the method was originated by Lang, the overall installation factors are often called Lang Factors L.

In this application, the main plant items are listed, sized, costed and summed to obtain the total main plant item cost ($MPIC$); the total installed cost C is then given by:

$$C = L \ (\Sigma MPIC)$$

or

$$C = (\Sigma MPIC) + (L-1) \ (\Sigma MPIC)$$

that is,

Total cost = equipment cost + installation cost

If the main plant items have been estimated correctly, their costs will take account of their scale; for early estimates, the exponential methods described in Section 4.4.5 could be used. Installation costs are also a function of scale but not necessarily to the same exponent as main plant item costs. If they were both to the same exponent, L would be constant for a specific type of plant. When costing a proposed plant, using data from very similar plant, accuracy may be improved by noting that L is inversely proportional to the tenth root of scale (approximately), $L \ \alpha \ 1/Q^{0.1}$.

Lang factors can be used as derived from Table 4.4 or from historical cost data. (Approximate factors can be derived from Table 4.4 by dividing the values by 100). The approach is quite reliable if data is available for a plant that is very similar to the proposed plant. It is necessary to know the basis of the historical cost — for example, is it an achieved cost or an estimate, battery limits or greenfield?

Lang factors, L, vary from about two to 10 depending on the process, scale, materials of construction and location. For UK projects, L varies from about 2.5 to about 5.5 and is typically 4.0, although much depends on whether the plant is solids, solids/fluids or fluids processing. It should be noted that transportation and management costs can be a high proportion of total cost for overseas locations in the developing world, so Lang factors will be greater in these cases.

4.5.4 Total plant erected cost using different installation factors for different main plant items

The installation factors for different main plant items (MPI) are not identical, so an improvement in accuracy could be obtained by applying individual installation factors F to individual $MPIs$ — that is, the erected cost of *one* main plant item c is given by:

$$c = F(MPIC) = (MPIC) + (F-1)\,(MPIC)$$

This is sometimes called the *modular* approach.

The installed cost of all the $MPIs$ is then given by:

$$C = \Sigma c$$

4.5.5 Main plant item installed cost using installation sub-factors

A variety of engineering activities are necessary to install a specific MPI. These can be assessed separately, so that for an item made wholly of carbon steel:

$$F = 1 + f_{erection} + f_{piping} + f_{instruments} + f_{electrical} + f_{civil}$$

$$+ f_{structures\ and\ buildings} + f_{lagging}$$

and the total installed cost c of this carbon steel MPI is given by:

$$c = (MPIC)\,(F)$$

$$= (MPIC)\,[1 + f_{er} + f_p + f_i + f_{el} + f_c + f_{sb} + f_l]$$

The numerical values of these factors are given in Table 4.5 (see pages 42–45). If an item is made from an 'exotic' material of construction that is not carbon steel, then the factor cannot be used directly. A *material factor* (f_m) can be defined by:

$$f_m = \frac{\text{cost of } MPI \text{ in exotic material}}{\text{cost of } MPI \text{ in carbon steel}} = \frac{MPIC_x}{MPIC}$$

It is usually true that only the purchase cost of the MPI and its associated pipework are altered by the use of an exotic material; the rest of the installation costs are the same whether the item is made from carbon steel or an exotic material. Separating these two classes of costs gives:

$$c = (MPIC)\,[(1 + f_p) + (f_{er} + f_i + f_{el} + f_c + f_{sb} + f_l)] \text{ (carbon steel items only)}$$

Applying a material factor (f_m) to the MPI and its associated piping only, the total erected cost of an exotic material MPI is:

$$c_x = (MPIC)\,[(1 + f_p)\,f_m + (f_{er} + f_i + f_{el} + f_c + f_{sb} + f_l)] \text{ (for any material)}$$

or in terms of the cost of the MPI in exotic material ($MPIC_x$):

Table 4.5 Installation sub-factors for main plant items

Value of individual main plant and item standardized to carbon steel basis £(January 2000). (Vessels, furnaces, machines and drives and materials handling equipment)

Main plant items (delivered)

Main plant items erection (f_{er})	Much of site erection included in purchase cost of equipment such as large tanks
	Average erection
	Equipment involving some site fabrication such as large pumps requiring lining up and serpentine coolers
	Equipment involving much site fabrication or fitting such as large distillation columns and furnaces
	(At discretion of estimator, interpolation may be made)

Piping, ducting and chutes including erection (f_p)	Ducting and chutes
	Small bore piping or service piping only
	Average bore piping and service piping such as predominantly liquid piping
	Large bore piping and service piping such as predominantly gas and vapour piping or
	Average bore piping with complex system such as much manifolding and recirculation
	Large bore piping complex system such as much manifolding and recirculation
	Multiply piping factors by 1.3 if steam tracing needed (or if exotic material not known)

Instruments (f_i)	Local instruments only
	— one controller and instruments
	— two controllers and instruments
	— three or more controllers and instruments

Electrical (f_{el})	Lighting only
	Lighting and power for ancillary drives such as conveyors, stirred vessels and air coolers
	Lighting and power excluding transformers and switchgear — that is, equipment off site — for machine main drives such as pumps, compressors and crushers
	Lighting and power including transformers and switchgear for machine main drives such as pumps, compressors and crushers

Item reference	£						
	Over 300,000	100,000 to 300,000	40,000 to 100,000	20,000 to 40,000	6000 to 20,000	3000 to 6000	Under 3000
	1.0	1.0	1.0	1.0	1.0	1.0	1.0
1	.013	.03	.04	.06	.075	.09	.25
2	.05	.08	.10	.11	.13	.15	.38
3	.08	.10	.13	.15	.18	.20	.48
4	.30	.38	.45	.56	.67	.77	1.13
5	.03	.05	.10	.18	.28	.43	.59
6	.06	.13	.26	.43	.69	1.04	1.40
7	.16	.26	.40	.66	.98	1.40	1.76
8	.20	.33	.49	.78	1.11	1.58	1.94
9	.25	.41	.61	.96	1.38	1.96	2.43
10							
11	.03	.04	.06	.13	.24	.43	.75
12	.09	.13	.22	.34	.49	.65	1.00
13	.13	.20	.33	.45	.60	.79	1.14
14	.18	.33	.43	.60	.77	.96	1.38
15	.03	.03	.03	.06	.10	.13	.19
16	.10	.14	.20	.26	.34	.41	.60
17	.13	.18	.25	.33	.43	.51	.63
18	.19	.25	.34	.46	.60	.74	1.00

Continued overleaf

Table 4.5 Installation sub-factors for main plant items (continued)

	Value of individual main plant and item standardized to carbon steel basis £(January 2000). (Vessels, furnaces, machines, drives and materials handling equipment)
Civil (f_c)	Average civil work, including plant and structure foundations, floors and services
	Above average civil work, complicated machine blocks, special floor protection, elevator pits in floors and considerable services.
	Multiply civil factor by 1.3 to allow for piling plant and structure foundations
Structures and buildings (f_{sb})	Negligible structural work and buildings
	Open air plant at ground level with some pipebridges and minor buildings
	Open air plant within a structure
	Plant in a simple covered building
	Plant in an elaborate building on a major structure within a building
Lagging (f_l)	Lagging for service pipes only
	Average amount of hot lagging on pipes and vessels
	Above average amount of hot lagging on pipes and vessels
	Cold lagging on pipes and vessels

This table must be used only with main plant items at purchase cost as if of carbon steel at January 2000.

The factors in this table are the same as those published in the third edition. But the instrumentation factor, f_i, may be low for plant systems with complex control schemes. In these circumstances, it is suggested that the factor is increased by 15–20%.

$$c_x = (MPIC_x) [(1 + f_p) + (f_{er} + f_i + f_{el} + f_c + f_{sb} + f_l)/f_m]$$

A table of such installation sub-factors (derived from the ICI FACTEST package) is given in Table 4.5. It can be seen that they are a function of:

(a) type of installation activity;
(b) complexity or difficulty of that activity;
(c) main plant item cost on the basis of the cost of the equivalent carbon steel item in £(January, 2000).

		£					
Item reference	**Over 300,000**	**100,000 to 300,000**	**40,000 to 100,000**	**20,000 to 40,000**	**6000 to 20,000**	**3000 to 6000**	**Under 3000**
19	.08	.10	.14	.17	.22	.28	.35
20	.15	.21	.31	.40	.50	.60	.85
21							
22	.012	.025	.025	.04	.05	.06	.08
23	.06	.08	.10	.14	.17	.21	.26
24	.14	.24	.31	.41	.50	.59	.74
25	.19	.29	.39	.48	.56	.69	.85
26	.35	.48	.63	.76	.90	1.06	1.38
27	.012	.03	.04	.06	.10	.15	.23
28	.03	.04	.08	.14	.21	.31	.38
29	.04	.06	.10	.17	.26	.35	.40
30	.06	.10	.15	.25	.31	.41	.56

The implications of (a) and (b) are obvious but (c) merits some explanation. One effect of restricting Table 4.5 to the cost of equivalent carbon steel equipment is to allow a single set of sub-factors to be used, in conjunction with material factors, to cover all exotic equipment. With this restriction, the main plant item cost becomes an indirect measure of scale which, in turn, allows the sub-factors to be a function of scale. Since inflation would distort the relationship between main plant item cost and sub-factors, Table 4.5 can only be valid at a specific date, which is January 2000 in this case.

When using Table 4.5 to make a capital cost estimate, the following procedure should be followed:

(a) list all of the main plant items;
   then for every MPI:
(b) estimate its size or rating;
(c) estimate its purchase cost (*MPIC* or *MPIC$_x$*), see Chapter 7;
(d) specify its material factor (for example, mild steel $= 1$, stainless steels $= 2$–4 and so on);
(e) convert *MPIC$_x$* to carbon steel basis;
(f) convert *MPI* carbon steel basis estimated cost to £(January 2000). Use a cost index, if necessary, see Chapter 8;
(g) select appropriate sub-factors from Table 4.5;
(h) calculate its installed cost using either:

$$c \text{ or } c_x = (MPIC)\,[(1 + f_p)\,f_m + (f_{er} + f_i + f_{el} + f_c + f_{sb} + f_l)] \quad \text{or}$$

$$(MPIC_x)\,[(1 + f_p) + (f_{er} + f_i + f_{el} + f_c + f_{sb} + f_l)/f_m]$$

(i) calculate total equipment erected cost using: $C = \Sigma c + \Sigma c_x$;
(j) adjust C from £(January 2000) to current £, using a cost index;
(k) to obtain total erected cost (TEC), add 15% for engineering design and supervision and 10% for management overheads. An amount for contingency can be added here too;
(l) to obtain total capital employed (TCE), add 5% for commissioning costs and 15% for working capital provision.

Please note that these allowances for engineering, overheads, commissioning and working capital are 'round-figure' values and are very significant components of the total cost of a project. In every particular project, these matters will be subject to close scrutiny and evaluation in accordance with each company's policies and the prevailing circumstances including, for example, project size and the extent to which techniques such as computer-aided design and integrated management systems are applied and the impact these have on a project's cost.

Example

(1) A heat transfer duty involving a process liquid and refrigerated brine requires a carbon steel exchanger. Its purchase price is estimated to be £51,000 (January 2000) and it will be installed at ground level. Appropriate MPI and installation sub-factors from Table 4.5 are:

	Factor	*Table 4.5 item reference*
MPIC = £51K	1.0	Column £40K–£100K
Erection	0.1	Item 2, average
Piping	0.4	Item 7, average
Instruments	0.22	Item 12, one controller
Electrical	0.03	Item 15, lighting only
Civil	0.14	Item 19, average
Structures and buildings	0.025	Item 22, negligible
Lagging	0.15	Item 30, refrigerated
TOTAL	2.065	

Thus the estimated installed cost, net of design, overheads and so on, is:

£51,000 × 2.065 = £105,000 at January 2000.

(2) If it is decided the above duty requires an exchanger that is identical except the tubes must be made from stainless steel type 304, where the material factor (f_m) is 2.2 and its estimated purchase price will be:

£51,000 × 2.2 = £112,200 at January 2000.

However, its estimated purchase price on a carbon steel basis will still be £51,000 so the sub-factors given above are still valid. If it is assumed that process piping will also be of SS304, the installed cost of the heat exchanger will be:

£51,000 [(1.0 + 0.4) 2.2 + (2.065 − 1.0 − 0.4)] = £191,000 at January 2000.

The total erected cost of a complete plant would be determined by applying the procedure to each of the main plant items, taking the summation of the results and then adding factors for engineering and management overheads as discussed above.

Used by experienced engineers, the factorial method of estimation can give estimates with a high probability of being comparable in accuracy to those obtained by more detailed and elaborate methods, but in a fraction of the time.

4.6 Detailed estimating

Detailed estimates are usually required to enable a contractor to make a firm commitment to the client and for a company to give approval to a project. Therefore, they have to be carried out to a greater accuracy than that required previously. As pointed out earlier, a considerable amount of engineering design work is necessary to prepare this type of estimate and very significant costs can be incurred in the preparation of the required information.

The plan, topography and soil-bearing properties of the site must be established and a plot plan developed to show the size and location of buildings, structures, roads, railways, main service runs, drains and fences. Drawings are also prepared to show architectural and construction details of buildings and structures.

Flow sheets and heat balances must be developed fully, utilities specified and decisions made as to how they will be provided. Piping and instrumentation drawings are made to illustrate the proposed control philosophies.

Engineering specifications are required for all standard equipment items and detailed drawings must be made for any special items. Arrangement drawings are required to show the location of equipment within buildings or structures and also in relation to other equipment.

Pipe sizes, materials of construction and jointing are specified, pipe runs worked out and arrangement drawings prepared. Specifications are made for all instruments, electric drives, substations and so on, and drawings produced to show their general arrangement and individual runs. Lagging such as insulation and painting specifications is also prepared.

Material take-offs are carried out for electrics, instrumentation, piping and valves, structures, insulation and paint, and all will be individually priced. Bills of quantities are prepared for civil work, foundations and buildings and sent to suitable sub-contractors for competitive bids. Construction in the field, which represents a significant proportion of the total installed cost, is considered in detail. Whenever possible, quantities, equipment, weights and locations, heavy lifts and site fabrication necessary are defined to allow construction specialists to be invited to bid on a sub-contractor basis.

When all of the cost data has been co-ordinated an estimate may be summarized as shown later in Table 5.1, page 56.

4.7 Computer cost estimating

There are two main ways of using a computer in costing activities. The first is for the calculation of the cost given a correlation, a curve fit or more rigorous model. The second is to use it to analyse a set of historical costs in the hope of discerning important cost trends.

Programs for the first task include the Icarus Corporation's Process Evaluator and Project Manager packages. The first includes an expert system, the second is linked to a scheduler. For educational use, the Chem Eng Software program also gives indicative costs. Many mass/energy balance simulators have costing routines included and there are plenty of in-house (and commercially secret) programs used by contractors and large manufacturing companies.

To analyse cost records, most spreadsheets have statistical packages and numerical optimizers included. As noted earlier, the power law or exponential equation is commonly found to work well:

$$C = k\, S^n$$

This can be extended to a multivariable form:

$$C = k\, S_1^{n1}\, S_2^{n2}\, S_3^{n3}\, \dots$$

where S_1, S_2 and so on are independent measures of size — for example, height and diameter of a vessel. This equation is easily linearized.

A simple extension of these forms is to add a further constant, k', to represent the fixed cost element:

$$C = k' + k\, S^n$$

and

$$C = k' + k\, S_1^{n1}\, S_2^{n2}\, S_3^{n3}\, \dots$$

Occasionally, linear and quadratic equations will give a reasonable fit too.

Recently, Petley and Edwards[9] have shown the use of fuzzy matching to be useful in costing complete chemical plant, and Gerrard[10] has used this approach together with neural networks and rational polynomials to provide equipment cost predictions. A number of expert systems are also available.

References in Chapter 4

1. Wilson, G.T., 1971, Capital investment for chemical plant, *Brit Chem Eng*, 16(10): 931–934.
2. Allen, D.H. and Page, R.C., 1975, Revised technique for predesign cost estimating, *Chem Eng*, pp 142–150.
3. Wessel, H.E., 1952, *Chemical Engineering*, July: 209, and 1953, January: 168–171, 200.
4. Hill, R.D., 1956, What petrochemical plants cost, *Petroleum Refiner*, 35(8): 106–110.
5. Zevnik, F.C. and Buchanan, R.L., 1963, Generalised correlation for process investment, *Chem Eng Prog*, 59(2): 70–77.
6. Taylor, J.H., 1977, The 'process step scoring' method for making quick capital estimates, *Engineering and Process Economics 2*, pp 259.
7. Timms, S.R.M., 1980, *M Phil Thesis* (Aston University).
8. Bridgwater, A.V. and Mumford, C.J., 1979, *Waste Recycling and Pollution Control Handbook*, Chapter 20 (George Godwin, UK).
9. Petley, G.J. and Edwards, D.W., 1995, Further developments in chemical plant costing using fuzzy matching, *Computers and Chemical Engineering*, 19 supplement, S675–S680. (Part of ESCAPE5 conference, 11–14 June 1995).
10. Gerrard, A.M. and Brass, J., 1999, Preliminary cost modelling for process vessels, *Proceedings of the 9th International Conference on Flexible Automation and Intelligent Manufacturing, Tilburg, Netherlands* (Begell House, New York).

Appendix to Chapter 4 – Application of step count capital cost estimating procedures to an acetic anhydride process

(See Section 4.3, page 21, and Figures 4.4 and 4.5, page 25).

The process parameters are as follows:

Capacity	20,000 tpy (44.8 million lb/y)
Number of functional units	5
Number of main plant items	26
Reactor conversion	0.126
Maximum process temperature	714°C (987°K)
Maximum process pressure	1.7 atm
Materials of construction	Lower grade of stainless steel

All estimates are presented in £(2000) for a battery limits plant.

A4.1 Wilson

$$C = 20.75\, f\, n\, (AUC)\, F_M F_P F_T$$

where,

AUC $= 21 V^{0.67}$
     $= 21(20,000)^{0.675}$ (taking V as the plant capacity instead of average equipment item throughput due to lack of data)
     $= 16,804$
f $= 2.0$
n $= 26$
F_M $= 1.3$
F_P $= 1.0$
F_T $= 1.12$

$\quad C = £26.40$ million (2000)

A4.2 Zevnik and Buchanan

$$C = 7470\,N\,Q^{0.6}\,10^{[(0.1\,\log P_{max}) + (1.8 \times 10^{-4}\,(T_{max} - 300)) + (Fm)]}$$

$$= 7470 \times 5\,(20{,}000)^{0.6}\,10^{(0.023 + 0.124 + 0.1)}$$

$$= £25.10\text{ million, }2000$$

A4.3 Taylor

In this procedure it is necessary to determine the Costliness Index of the process by considering significant process steps, and assessing scores to their parameters as below:

Significant process step	Score								Total score	Costliness index
	a	b	c	d	e	f	g	h		
Feed storage	–	–	2	0	0	0	0	0	2	1.7
Reaction	2	0	–	2	0	2	0	0	6	4.8
Quench	3	–	–	1	0	2	0	0	6	4.8
Absorber	1	–	–	0	0	1	0	0	2	1.7
Crude product storage	–	–	2	0	0	1	0	0	3	2.2
Acetone still	3	–	–	0	0	1	0	0	4	2.9
Acetic anhydride still	1	–	–	0	0	1	0	0	2	1.7
Product storage	–	–	2	0	0	1	0	0	3	2.2
									Total	22.0 (rounded)

Key
a — relative throughput, t/t product
b — reaction time in hours
c — storage time in weeks
d — temperature extreme
e — pressure extreme
f — materials of construction
g — multi-streaming
h — special problems

Costliness index (Ci) for whole process = 20.8

and $C = 379{,}680\,(Q)^{0.39}\,Ci$

where Q is plant capacity in thousands of tonnes.
Then,

$$C = 379{,}680 \ (20)^{0.39} \ 20.8$$

$$= £25.40 \text{ million, } 2000$$

A4.4 Timms

(a) Simple equation:

$$C = 10560 \ N \ Q^{0.615}$$

$$= 10560 \times 5 \ (20{,}000)^{0.615}$$

$$= £23.32 \text{ million, } 2000$$

(b) With materials of construction, temperature and pressure effects:

$$C = 4910 \ N \ Q^{0.639} \ Fm \ (T_{max})^{0.066} \ (P_{max})^{-1.016}$$

$$= 4910 \times 5 \times 560.2 \times 1.2 \times 1.58 \times 0.99$$

$$= £25.8 \text{ million, } 2000$$

A4.5 Bridgwater

This is not strictly applicable as it is only for liquid/solid processes, but is included for illustration. It is generally found that solid or solid-liquid processing steps cost significantly more than gas and gas-liquid steps and consequently it would be expected that this model will give a high value for the estimated capital cost.

$$£C = 1930 \ N \left(\frac{Q}{s}\right)^{0.675}$$

$$= 1930 \times 5 \left(\frac{20{,}000}{0.125}\right)^{0.675}$$

$$= £31.26 \text{ million, } 2000$$

A4.6 Discussion

The step count order-of-magnitude estimate models have yielded answers in the range £23.32 million to £31.26 million (2000) with a mean value of £25.28 million (ignoring the estimate from the liquid-solid system model); the results are summarized in Table A4.1 (overleaf). These values are compared with an estimate prepared by another method which gave a value of £27.12 million ±25%. Thus, at order-of-magnitude level of estimating, the step count models may be judged to have yielded an acceptable result.

One of the most significant sources of error lies in updating cost models and cost data over long periods of time, and particularly when location changes are also involved. (The models given in this Appendix have been adjusted for these effects whenever possible, as explained in Chapter 8).

Table A4.1 Summary of step count order-of-magnitude capital cost estimates for acetic anhydride plant

	Phase limitations	Capital cost, UK £million	Deviation from average cost, %	Deviation from mean estimated cost by other method
1. Wilson	G	26.40	+4.43	−2.66
2. Zevnik and Buchanan	G	25.10	−0.73	−7.46
3. Taylor	G, L, S	25.40	0.48	−6.33
4. Timms	G	23.32	−7.75	−14.00
5. Timms	G	25.80	+2.03	−4.89
6. Bridgwater	L, S	31.26	23.65	15.26
Average		25.28		−6.78
A new independent estimate made in 2000		27.12 ± 25%	7.28	

Presenting the complete estimate

5

5.1 Introduction

Projects may vary in character from a new research-based development to the duplication of an existing plant; a greenfield project to a major modification of an operating plant; improving utilities to upgrading a main production line; and from a simple to a highly complex integrated project. Whatever the project, the same basic estimating procedures can be applied to all these situations.

The validity of an estimate depends upon all relevant items being accounted for. This is particularly important when evaluating new processes resulting from research and development, as over-optimistic — that is, low — estimates can easily be produced by omitting items such as the ancillary services which are invariably required. These omissions produce the classic cases of projects whose costs increase dramatically during development. Equally important is the need to avoid high estimates, which may arise from the inclusion of unnecessary refinements. These could erroneously cause a project to be rejected.

The formulation and layout of cost estimates is a matter for company policy and is related to the type of plant and the company code of accounts. In addition to the conventional range of capital cost items described in this Guide which are summarized in Table 5.1 (overleaf), a number of special items may need to be considered. These include:

(a) Costs relating directly to the purchase and use of the project site itself, to be added to the engineering and home office costs, and may include wayleaves, compensation, and legal charges.
(b) Credits may be derived from investment grants, employment premiums, taxation allowances and other Government legislative procedures. It is important to ensure that the costs incurred in obtaining these incentives do not exceed the benefits.
(c) In the case of overseas contracts, the price will be modified to take into account the additional cost associated with local import duties, taxes, rules, laws, ways of doing business, and the political and social systems.

Table 5.1 Example breakdown of a detailed estimate

A	**Equipment**	Cost £	
	Furnaces		
	Package plants		
	Heat exchangers		
	Air coolers		
	Compressors and fans		
	Pumps and drivers		
	Turbines		
	Tanks		
	Vessels		
	Columns and reactors		
	Miscellaneous equipment items		
	SUBTOTAL A:	_____	= Main plant item cost
B	**Bulk items**		
	Electrics		
	Instrumentation		
	Computer control system		
	Piping and valves		
	Structures		
	Insulation and paint		
	Catalysts, chemical and oils		
	SUBTOTAL B:	_____	
C	**Civil works**		
	Roads		
	Foundations		
	Piling		
	Buildings		
	SUBTOTAL C:	_____	
D	**Construction**		
	Labour and sub-contracts		
	Site supervision		
	Tools, rentals and so on		
	SUBTOTAL D:	_____	
	SUBTOTAL A + B + C + D:	_____	= Installed plant cost
E	**Home office costs**		
	Procurement		
	Engineering		
	Project management		
	Expenses		
	SUBTOTAL E:	_____	
F	**Contingency and risk allowances**		
G	**Forward inflation in cost**		
	GRAND TOTAL A–G	£ _____	= Total plant cost

A typical summary estimate is given in Table 5.1 and an estimating checklist is shown in the Appendix, page 62.

5.2 Contingency

The checklist given in the appendix is extensive and its systematic application should result in a comprehensive estimate. However, every estimate has a margin of error associated with it and no matter how much detailed work has been carried out, the end result is still an estimate, not a statement of cost. The magnitude of the variation between the estimated and actual cost depends on a number of factors, each of which should be considered quite separately, namely:

- quality of the scope definition of the project;
- quality and reliability of cost data available for the estimate;
- extent and accuracy of design and the material take-offs;
- validity of any quotations received and the estimating methods used;
- unknown cost factors such as transport costs;
- changes in inflation and cost escalation;
- currency exchange rate fluctuations;
- location and nature of the site with problems such as unexpected foundation difficulties;
- local regulations;
- local labour problems, labour shortages and disputes;
- adverse weather during construction;
- subcontractors delays;
- organizational complexity of project (particularly for overseas projects).

Each factor should ideally be examined in detail, appraised using conventional statistical analysis and a final addition made to the base estimate. The more experienced cost estimators may have developed their own data for such calculations or have access to a company database. The less experienced will add a percentage according to the overall perceived degree of uncertainty which can range from zero through to a more typical 10% to 20% or up to 50%, depending on the confidence built up during the preparation of the estimate.

5.3 Future inflation

From the methods outlined, an assessment of the cost involved for carrying out the project work can be calculated. These costs will have been assessed using prices ruling at the applicable date of any quotation or on statistics that have been updated to current price levels. However, it is necessary to forecast inflation throughout the life of the contract. It is essential to establish trends using the typical indices suggested in Chapter 8 or to utilize the various contract price adjustment formulae available, again using appropriate indices as necessary.

5.4 Exchange rate variation

It is possible to account for at least a major part of the uncertainty in exchange rate variability by 'buying forward'. This involves a contract to buy a specified amount of foreign currency at a specified rate at a specified date in the future. The exchange rate agreed will account for the perceived variation in inflation rates, interest rates and other economic factors in both or all countries covered. LIFFE (London International Financial Futures and Options Exchange) specializes in this area, which is complex and should be dealt with through experts in this field.

5.5 Working capital

Working capital can be defined as the funds, in addition to the fixed capital, land investment and start-up costs, which a company must provide in a project to get started and meet obligations such as wages and costs of raw materials as they come due, until income is received from sales. Accountants define working capital as current assets less current liabilities and it is the sum of cash, accounts receivable and inventory, less taxes and accounts payable.

Working capital typically includes: wages, salaries and purchased services for a period of one to three months; stock in stores, adequate raw materials such as feed tank and bunkers half full of raw materials; materials in process, stock of finished product equal to one half of storage capacity; and fuel for a period of one to three months (but all these amounts will probably be greater for an overseas project in an undeveloped area). It is conventionally estimated in a number of ways:

(a) a percentage of the fixed capital investment: typically taken as 15%, but it is more for small projects and less for large projects; often in the range of 10%–30% of fixed investment, respectively; or

(b) several months operating costs, typically three to six months; or

(c) several months gross income, typically two to four months.

Note that working capital will need to be increased each year with inflation, together with other changes, such as increased capacity. It is usually entirely recovered in the last year of operation of the project.

Working capital may vary widely depending on the nature of the product and its cost of manufacture. When working capital becomes significantly high, it plays an important part in the calculation of profitability.

5.6 Scrap value

Although some companies, as a matter of policy, attribute a scrap value to the plant at the end of its useful life, in practice this is not sensible. The scrap value is unlikely to be significant; it will also arise some considerable time into the future with a consequently small discounted effect on plant profitability. If profitability is dependent on such a relatively small sum arising well into the future, then the project risks are very high!

In practical terms, the scrap value of the plant is likely to be more or less matched by the cost of dismantling. If buildings can be reused, they may have some value. Some items of plant may also be transferred to other projects or used as spares and these also have some scrap value. Finally, exotic materials of construction and materials, such as catalysts, can have a substantial scrap value which also need to be estimated. Briggs *et al.* give a more in-depth analysis of decommissioning[1].

5.7 Commissioning costs

There are several steps involved in what is often referred to as commissioning:

(1) Precommissioning: a check to make sure the system is ready to accept process fluids and includes inspection, washing out and pressure testing.

(2) Mechanical commissioning: ensures that moving parts such as pumps move in the correct direction, valves work and all mechanical and electrical engineering systems are working satisfactorily.

(3) Process commissioning: involves items such as instrumentation and control testing. It is concerned with the operation of the entire plant or major sections of plant in an integrated way rather than as separate items of equipment.

(4) Start-up: process materials are fed into the process and the system gradually brought to full operation.

These commissioning costs consist of fixed and variable costs. Fixed costs include operating, maintenance and supervisory staff and overhead charges. Variable costs include raw materials (which might be increased by a low efficiency in the initial period of plant operation), and services such as water, steam, compressed air and power. Materials and services may be used on trials which do not produce saleable product.

These should be estimated in as much detail as possible and a decision taken as to whether they should be charged to capital or revenue, or apportioned between the two. The net cost of commissioning is the sum of fixed and variable costs less the value of any good product made up to the time when the plant is producing according to acceptance criteria set out in the contract.

Commissioning times can vary widely from a few days to several months, depending on the type of plant, its novelty and the experience of the commissioning staff. Similarly, it is not possible to specify standard data for estimating commissioning costs, which may vary from 1% to 10% of the capital cost dependent upon the size, complexity and novelty of the plant. Wherever possible, commissioning costs should be estimated from a breakdown of the records of costs for previous plants of similar nature, preferably referring to the performance of the same or comparable contractors.

Contractors prefer to carry out the commissioning and start-up of plants utilizing their own experienced personnel and charge on a 'per diem' basis as it is extremely difficult to quantify the length of time they are likely to be involved. A typical hourly rate in 1999 for an experienced commissioning engineer would be approximately £75 , plus expenses. Therefore it is not difficult to understand why, in a highly complex plant, the commissioning costs can be high.

It is common practice for the contractor, in collaboration with the process licenser, to provide training facilities for the purchaser's operating and maintenance personnel especially if the purchaser is inexperienced in the use of highly technological processing plants. Limited numbers of the purchaser's key operating and maintenance staff can undergo training at the various works of the process licensers. This would include process familiarization comprising classroom instruction training with the aid of a process simulator and various plant visits and specific on-site training in operations procedures. These are usually charged at cost.

David Horsley's book on process plant commissioning provides useful guidance on this subject[2].

5.8 Changes of scope and cost control

In the development of any process, it should always be the aim to establish definitive basic data before starting design of the process plant. This aim is not always achieved in practice, so that it is wise to make a contingency allowance to cover for changes in scope during the project life. Large changes in the basic data will usually involve major rethinking of the whole plant. This should be avoided, as this situation can never be handled by the normal contingency allowance in an estimate, and it would rather call for a complete reappraisal and amended authorization.

Changes in scope fall into three basic categories: additions or deletions to the project, delays arising from these or by other deviations from the contract programme — for example, late deliveries of equipment or materials. Both the purchaser's and plant builder's project teams should endeavour to restrict variations and changes of scope to a minimum but inevitably they will arise and usually result in an increase in costs.

The project manager should be responsible for the continuing surveillance and cost control to keep these changes of scope to an absolute minimum. It cannot be emphasized strongly enough, and it must be continually borne in mind that cost control must be achieved by management and this means the management of the entire project. Monthly, or more frequently if circumstances warrant, and systematic reporting and scrutiny of the progress of the work are necessary to enable effective control to be carried out. The details highlighted in such reviews should point to the areas where corrective action is needed. It is this action, taken promptly, that is the real contribution to cost control. As soon as an unfavourable trend is discovered, management should take action. If action is delayed, time and money will have been expended, which usually cannot be recovered later.

It is not unusual to see the cost of changes of scope range up to 20% of the total original capital cost of the plant. This may be justifiable in the circumstances of a particular project but generally it will be unsatisfactory if a change in cost of this extent is not foreseen in a timely and accurate manner.

References in Chapter 5

1. Briggs, M., Buck, S. and Smith, M., 1997, *Decommissioning, Mothballing and Revamping* (IChemE, UK).
2. Horsley, D., 1998, *Process Plant Commissioning*, 2nd edn (IChemE, UK).

Appendix to Chapter 5
– An estimating checklist

A5.1 Site

Land purchase plus all associated costs arising from legal requirements
Soil survey
Survey of special site hazards such as earthquakes, susceptibility to flooding
and abnormal meteorological conditions
Road improvements and diversions
Railway improvements
Pipe track and other wayleaves
Dock and wharfage requirements
Water supply contribution
Sewage disposal works

A5.2 Process plant

All process plant and equipment from detailed schedules
Special erection costs — for example, clean conditions
Costs of special materials
Costs due to special manufacturing techniques or pressure on manufacturing
capacity
Inspection and testing
Delivery, particularly considering heavy, long or wide loads, heavy lifts and
special restrictions or consents
Catalysts and so on if they are to be charged as capital
Safety equipment
Containment of any hazardous operation
Ventilation, with particular reference to hot conditions, toxic gases and
vapours, dusts and fire risks
Fire protection equipment
Equipment to meet requirements of alkali inspector and factory inspector
Effluent treatment plants (including development costs)

Instrumentation and control
Development of instrumentation
Pipework and valves
Insulation and painting
Costs of process development and prototype testing
Allowance for modification after erection
Standby plant
Mechanical handling facilities

A5.3 Service plant and equipment

Steam raising plant and auxiliaries
Electricity connection charges
Transformers and switchgear
Cabling
Starters
Standby power supplies
Plant and pipework for storage and handling of water for process, cooling and
  potable supplies
Water treatment plant
Internal transport, conveying and storage of raw materials, intermediate
  finished products and fuel
Heating and lighting
Cranes, jibs, maintenance equipment
Test equipment
Lightning protection
Compressed air services
Refrigeration, local or centralized
Inert or special gas supplies
Operating and maintenance manuals, drawings and so on
Spares (in so far as chargeable to capital account)
Telephones and communications

A5.4 Civil works

Piling and soil stabilization
Foundations
Main plant buildings
Plant structural steelwork
Chimneys

Buildings for service plant
Stores, storage buildings, warehousing
Laboratories, workshops, offices
Medical and first aid centres, fire station
Canteen, change rooms, lavatories
Site security, fencing, gate houses
Garages, car parks, cycle sheds
Customs and excise offices, weighbridge
Drainage: surface, chemical and soil water
Pipe and cable ducts
Land reinstatement, landscaping and so on
Compliance with local and national regulations

A5.5 Overhead costs

Engineering costs
Process and detailed design, purchasing and inspection
Use of consultants or specialists
Departmental overheads
Construction of models
Lloyd's or special inspection
Travel
Engineering involvement in commissioning

Temporary facilities required for construction
Site engineer's office and furniture
Temporary power and water supplies
Temporary access and storage areas, fencing – site security
Construction workshops (can main project workshops be used?)
Site fabrication facilities and consumable materials
Labour camp – canteen
Major construction equipment (purchase or hire)

Direct construction costs
Direct labour or contract labour
Subsidies to labour – travelling, canteen and so on
Specialists' transport costs
Overtime working, abnormal weather conditions, local customs and regulations

Miscellaneous overhead items

Process or patent fees
Agent's fees
Consultant's fees
Proportion of company's research expenditure
Proportion of company's central administration expenditure
Miscellaneous local or federal taxes
Insurance
Financing charges
Legal costs
Import duties
Special freight costs
Contractor's overheads and profit.

Costing, economics and design

6

6.1 Economic design

Economic design of any process plant is of paramount importance. The products that are manufactured on such plants are sold in highly competitive markets, so the capital and operating costs of the plant must be kept to a minimum. The capital cost of a process plant indirectly affects overall production costs due to the depreciation factor and the bank interest charges which have to be taken into account. These are often major components in the build up of production costs.

Economic design is achieved more readily if the design and estimating engineers collaborate at an early stage in the evaluation of any project.

6.2 Standardization

A large proportion of the items that go into making up a process plant are now only available in standard sizes. Pumps, motors, valves, pipework materials, heat exchangers and so on are all manufactured to meet both international and the supplier's own manufacturing standards.

Standardization has become necessary for many reasons, not least of which is the need for the supplier to produce goods in the most economic manner, in order to match the intense competition from others.

6.3 Alternative designs

Although many items are of standard supply, alternatives can exist which are capable of the required duty. For instance, two pumps may be available where both are able to pump the required volume against the required head, but operating at different speeds. The slower speed pump will be larger and more expensive, but any price differential must be offset against the potentially higher maintenance costs of the higher speed pump. Similarly, space restrictions may be a major factor in the choice between two standard heat exchangers with the same surface area but different L/D ratios.

6.4 Process considerations

Process considerations can affect the choice between the use of one large unit or two smaller ones, each half the capacity. The use of two units in place of one larger one will usually be more expensive. Failure of a larger single unit results in a total loss of production. Where speciality chemicals are involved, the selection of two smaller units, either enabling some level of production to be sustained in the event of one unit failure, is often the appropriate approach. Each case should be examined for overall cost effectiveness before the final selection is made.

6.5 Specification standards

Some industries adopt higher standards than others, usually as a result of the hazards inherent in their manufacturing processes. For example, the petroleum industry and manufacturers of inflammable solvents are exposed to potential explosion and fire risks, while the pharmaceutical and food-orientated process industries have sterility factors to consider in order to avoid hazards to public health. These industries have developed their own standards over many years which, in most cases, have now been adopted universally. There are many suppliers of standard equipment which meet these special requirements, but many items are specific to the process and have been developed especially to meet a particular set of circumstances.

Process technology is constantly developing and changing and it is essential that the estimating engineer does not price a new project on the basis of using equipment which may be of a higher standard than is required.

6.6 Duty specification

The guaranteed performance of standard equipment must be carefully studied before selection is made. It is inevitable that borderline situations will be met where the upper limit of one size is just below that specified by the design engineer. The next standard size will have a capability much larger than requirement. The designer has almost certainly specified a duty with an in-built performance margin and very often the cheaper unit will meet a slightly revised specification by the designer, who is prepared to accept a reduced performance margin. In this way, the double rounding effect which would otherwise occur, can be avoided.

6.7 Operational standards

The operation of process plants must be carried out in a safe manner and the plant design must incorporate the necessary features to ensure that this is so. The disasters of Flixborough, Seveso and Bhopal serve to underline the importance of safety.

HAZOP studies are now carried out on plant designs before they are finalized, in order to eliminate potential danger areas[1,2]. However, economics are still considered in such studies since the ultimately safe plant is usually so expensive that the whole project is no longer viable.

A situation can arise where the only material of construction suitable against corrosion is, for example, titanium. The cost of fabrication in this and similar exotic materials is usually prohibitive. In such cases, a suitable grade of stainless steel may be available which corrodes at a known rate under the process operating conditions. The vessel would be fabricated in stainless steel, the thickness allowing for both stress and corrosion, and the working life is predetermined. Regular replacement is made after a suitable period of working, with careful inspection (including thickness measurements) made at suitable intervals during the vessel lifetime as an added precaution.

6.8 Cost optimization

The choice of construction material is not always determined by the conditions relating to individual items. For instance, in piping systems the choice of material used can affect the total installed cost, particularly when plastic materials are involved. Selection could be between the use of plastic pipelines or mild steel pipes, suitably lined. The latter may be more expensive but are more easily supported, whereas plastic pipes usually require supporting throughout their entire length. The overall installed cost of the lined pipe system could well be cheaper than that of the plastic pipe system.

Other factors affecting the selection of components and materials are plant location, energy conservation, and plant maintenance. Many plants today are built in developing countries where communication and access are limited, and where spare parts and fuel are not readily available so they often need to be imported. In such circumstances, selection should favour components and materials with a long working life and minimum maintenance requirements, particularly if the local maintenance skills are limited.

Energy is an important item of total production cost and should be conserved wherever possible. Energy consumption of components should be carefully considered and taken into account before final selection.

6.9 Process economics

An examination of costs may lead to conclusions which suggest ways of improving process economics. The development of ammonia synthesis process provides an interesting case study.

In 1963, a radical improvement to the process economics was made possible by the development of reliable high pressure centrifugal compressors. This, in turn, led to a much better use of process waste heat to generate steam for driving these compressors. Consequently, expensive electric motor-driven reciprocating compressors, generally provided with installed spares to cope with the known operational problems of these units, gave way to single centrifugal machines with no installed spares. Since centrifugal compressors work better with larger throughputs, this also led to a rapid increase in plant size. Before 1963, most plants were in the capacity range 300–400 tonne/d, with a few being supplied up to 600 tonne/d using reciprocating compressors. It was at 600 tonne/d output that the first ammonia plants with centrifugal compressors were supplied. However, within two or three years, plants of 1000 tonne/d capacity were proposed and, by 1970, a 1575 tonne/d plant had been ordered.

Although the combination of centrifugal compressor and back pressure steam turbine is more expensive in capital cost terms, the operating costs are considerably less than the equivalent electric motor system, and thus the former is the more economic alternative.

References in Chapter 6

1. European Process Safety Centre, 2000, *HAZOP: Guide to Best Practice* (IChemE, UK).
2. Kletz, T., 1999, *Hazop and Hazan*, 4th edn (IChemE, UK).

Cost curves for
preliminary estimates

7

This chapter features equipment cost graphs, all reported as 'delivered to site' (UK) in January 2000.

Figure 7.1 Package boiler

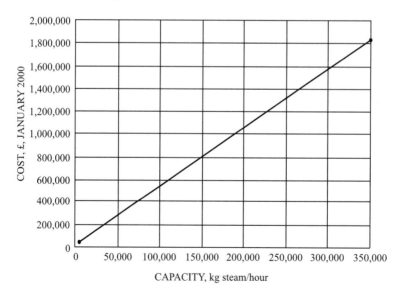

This applies to gas fired designs, for 20 bar g steam, with 55C of superheat. It is made of carbon steel and is skid mounted.

Figure 7.2 Field erected boiler

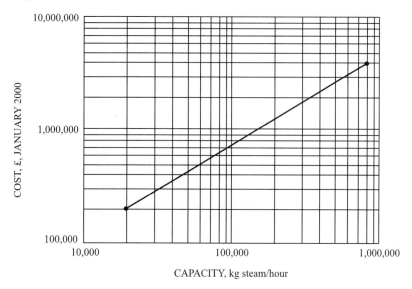

This applies to gas fired designs, for 30 bar g steam, with 60C of superheat. It is made of carbon steel.

Figure 7.3 Flare stack, derrick supported

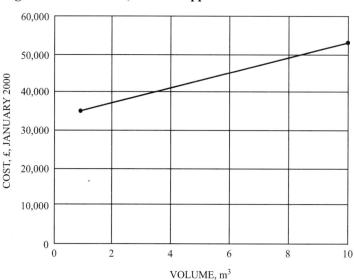

Figure 7.4 High pressure reactor

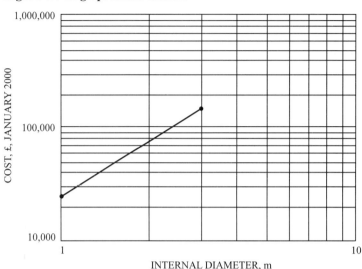

For the above curve, the pressure is 325 bar g with a reactor length of 20 m. The item is made of carbon steel. (If 316 stainless is used, then multiply the cost by a factor of 1.3.) This graph can also be used as an approximate guide to the cost of a pressure vessel of the dimensions shown above.

Figure 7.5 Insulated, agitated reactor vessel

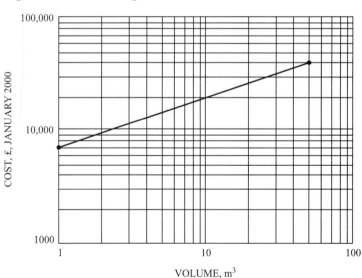

The above graph is for carbon steel, use multiplying factors of 1.6 and 1.7 to convert to 304 and 316 stainless steels. The pressure is 3 bar. At 10 bar g, the cost increases by a factor of about 1.9.

Figure 7.6 Gas cyclone

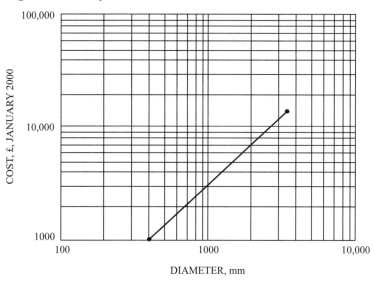

The chart is for a pressure of 1 bar g, with carbon steel materials. For 304 stainless steel, use a multiplying factor of about 1.8.

Figure 7.7 Pusher centrifuge

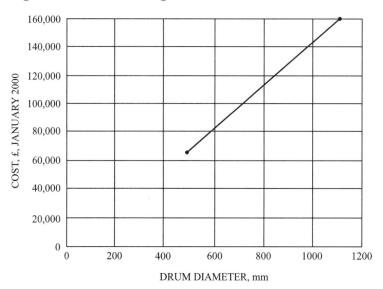

The material of construction is 316 stainless steel. The cost includes motor, gearbox and baseplate.

Figure 7.8 Decanter centrifuge

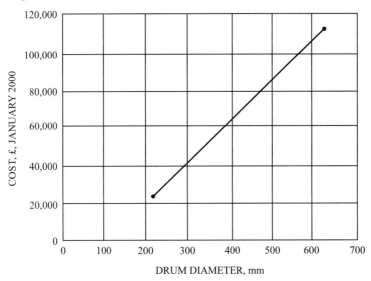

The material of construction is 316 stainless steel. The cost includes motor, gearbox and baseplate.

Figure 7.9 Peeler centrifuge

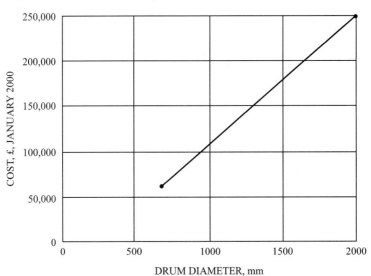

The material of construction is 316 stainless steel. The cost includes motor, gearbox and baseplate.

Figure 7.10 Pall rings

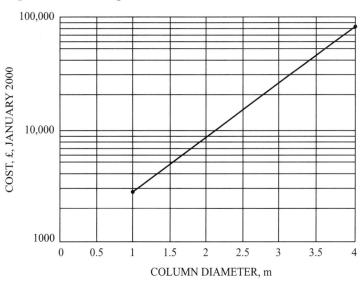

This is for a depth of 5 m of rings and includes support plate. For other depths, use 0.6 power law cautiously. The material of construction is 304 stainless steel. For 316 grade, use a multiplying factor of 1.1 and for polypropylene, use 0.3.

Figure 7.11 Structured packing, 5 m height

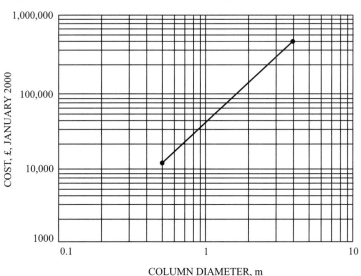

For 5 m of packing including support plates, in 304 stainless steel. For 316 stainless, multiply by 1.05. For other depths, use 0.6 power law cautiously.

Figure 7.12 Sieve trays

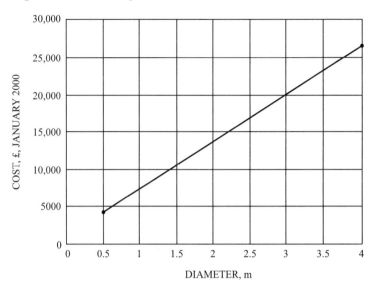

For TEN carbon steel trays. For 304 stainless, use a multiplying factor of 1.25 and for 316, use 1.35. Use 0.6 power law for other number of plates.

Figure 7.13 Valve trays

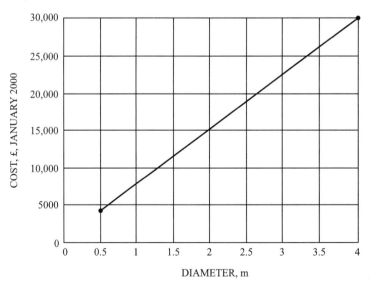

For TEN trays of carbon steel. For 304 stainless, multiply by 1.2, and for 316 stainless, use 1.4. Use 0.6 power law for other number of plates.

76

Figure 7.14 Columns

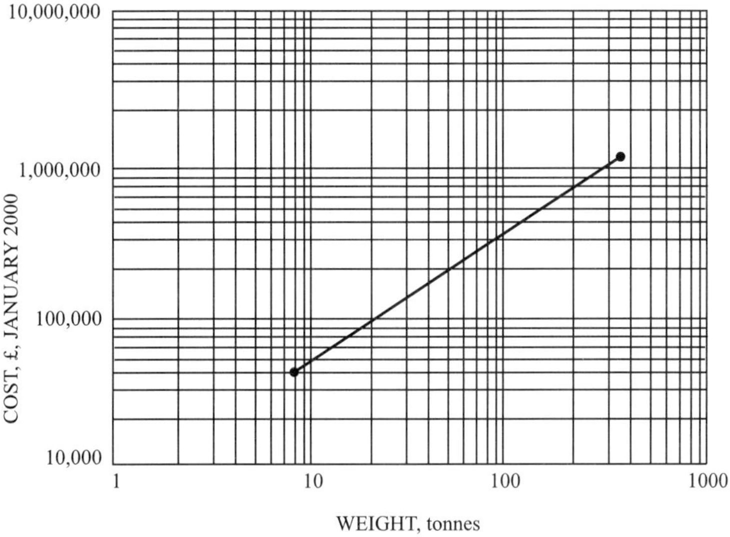

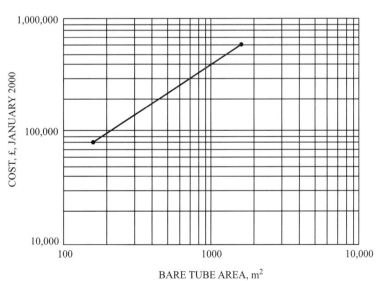

The material of construction is carbon steel, data applies to an empty shell.

Figure 7.15 Air cooled heat exchanger

The material of construction is carbon steel.

Figure 7.16 9% Ni pressure vessel

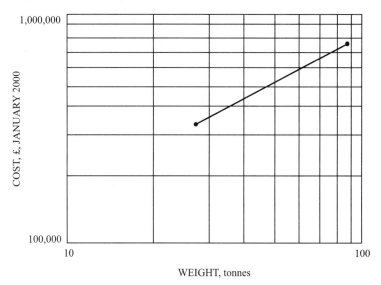

Applicable for wall thickness up to 30 mm.

Figure 7.17 Stainless steel pressure vessel

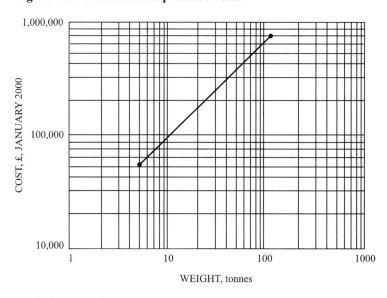

Applicable for wall thickness up to 60 mm.

Figure 7.18 Shell and tube heat exchangers

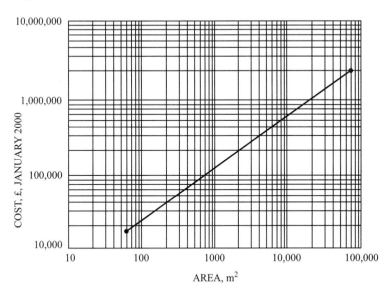

Material of construction is carbon steel.

Figure 7.19 Compressor

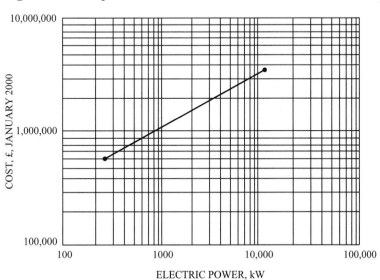

Compressor is handling petrochemicals. Costs include gear box, motor and baseplate.
Very approximate as data includes both reciprocal and centrifugal machines!

Figure 7.20 Pneumatic drier

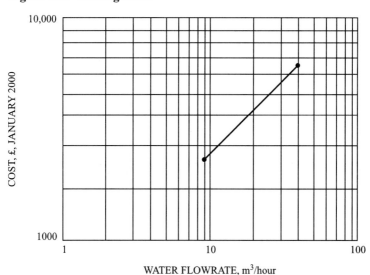

Includes gas fired air heater plus outlet gas cleaning equipment, made of 304L stainless steel.

Figure 7.21 Cooling tower

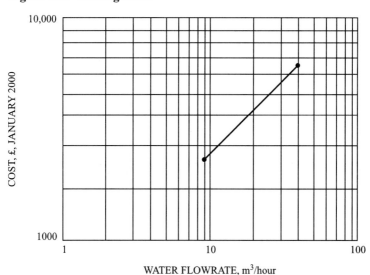

This is a forced convection tower, with fan cost included. The water is cooled by some 13C. Foundations and sump excluded.

Figure 7.22 Rotary drum filter

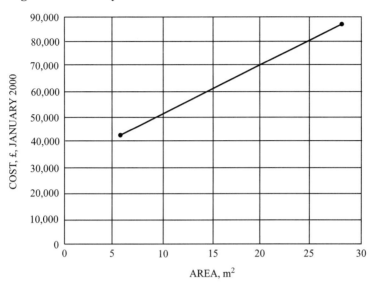

Material of construction is carbon steel. Cost excludes pumps.

Figure 7.23 Tank with steam coil

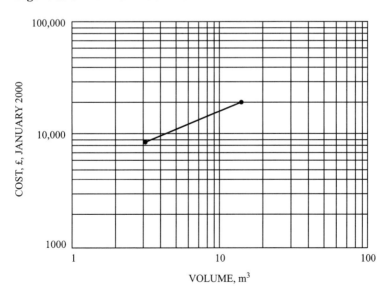

Material of construction is carbon steel.

Figure 7.24 Scrubber

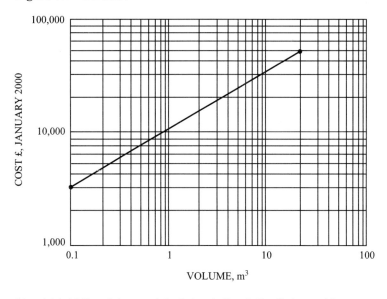

Material is 304L stainless steel. Includes shell and 1″ pall ring packing.

Figure 7.25 Atmospheric tanks

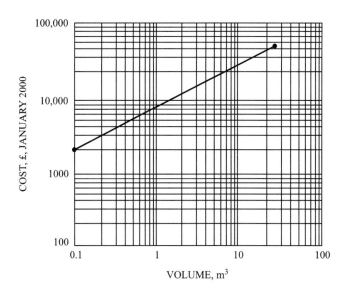

For atmospheric pressure made of 304L steel.

Figure 7.26 Large tank

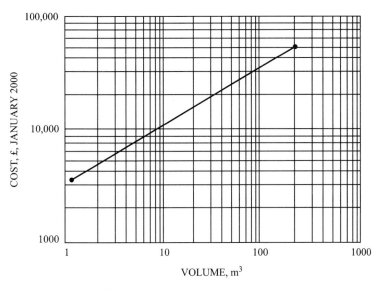

Material of construction is carbon steel.

Figure 7.27 Fans

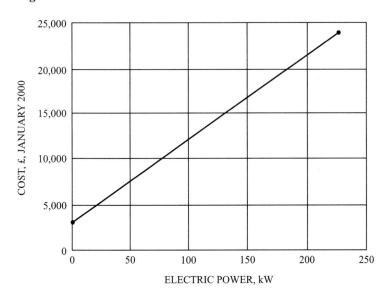

Carbon steel, cost includes motor.

Figure 7.28 Silo

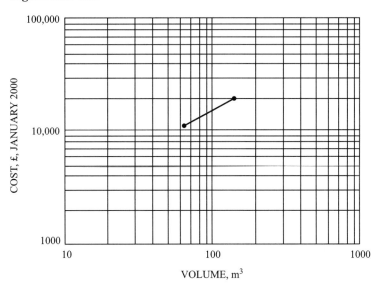

Constructed from mild steel.

Figure 7.29 Mixers

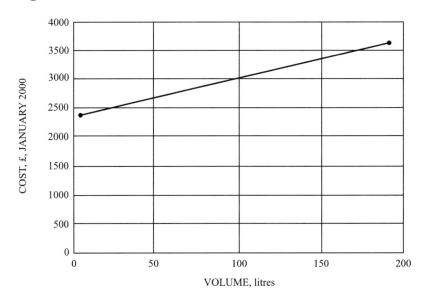

Note that the agitator is sized from vessel volume. material of construction is 316 stainless steel. Cost includes motor and agitator only.

Figure 7.30 Installed piping cost

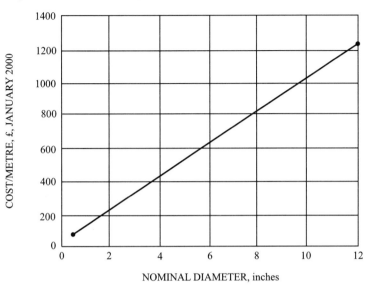

For stainless steel piping, very approximate! Note mixed units.

Figure 7.31 Piping, materials only

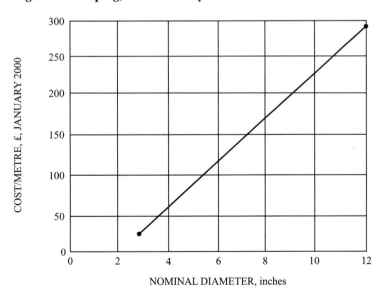

For stainless steel piping, very approximate! Note mixed units.

Figure 7.32 Gate valve

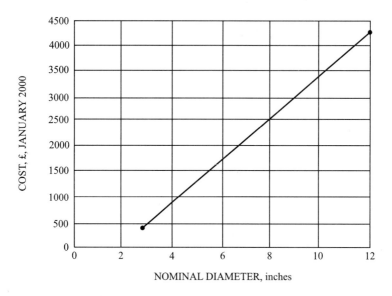

For stainless steel materials, very approximate!

Figure 7.33 Small centrifugal pump

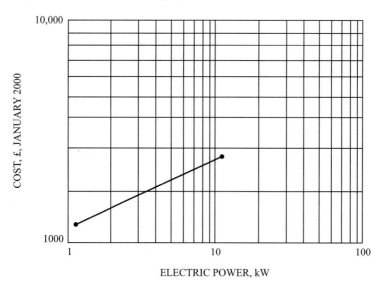

Cost includes motor. Material of construction is cast iron. For 316 stainless, use a factor of about 1.5.

Figure 7.34 Large centrifugal pump

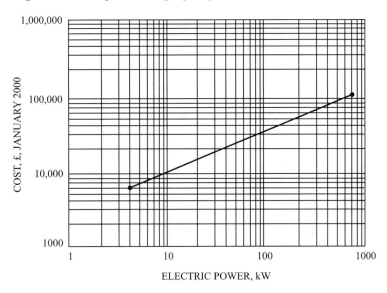

Material of construction is A216, a high temperature carbon steel, for A351(a chrome-nickel stainless steel), use a factor of about 3. Costs include gearbox, motor and baseplate.

Figure 7.35 Vacuum pump

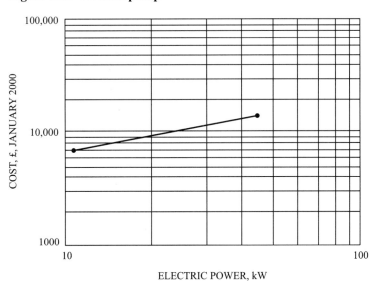

Cost includes motor. Material of construction is cast iron. For 316 stainless, use a factor of about 2.

Figure 7.36 Mono pump

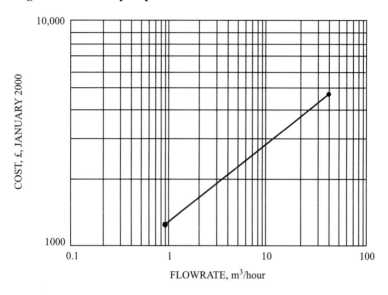

Cost includes motor. Main material of construction is cast iron.

Figure 7.37 Peristaltic pump

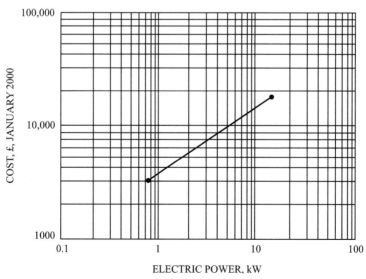

Cost includes motor. Main material of construction is cast iron.

Figure 7.38 Electric motors

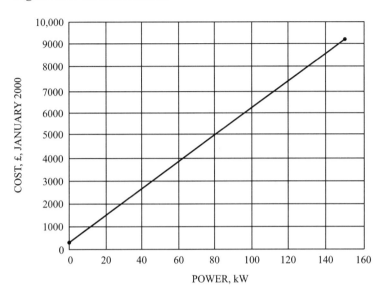

This graph applies to 3000 rpm, 2 pole, synchronous machines in a petrochemical environment.

Figure 7.39 Control valve

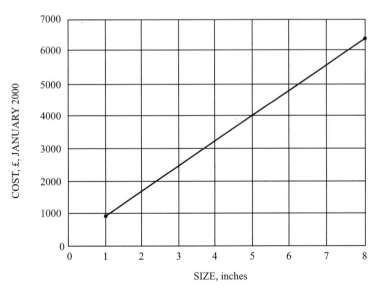

For a carbon steel valve and actuator.

Conclusions

These graphs give approximate costs for a range of new equipment. Occasionally, it may be found advantageous to purchase items on the secondhand market. There is a worldwide trade in such equipment. The asking price is often about half the new cost. If the equipment has been refurbished and comes complete with a warranty, the fraction may rise to around two thirds.

The IChemE companion text by Sweeting discusses handling uncertainty in cost data[1]. Briefly, the key quantity is the coefficient of variation, cv, which is the ratio of standard deviation to the mean. Table 7.9 of that text suggests it is often a small, fractional number. Once cv has been estimated, a probability distribution function is used — for example, the gamma or log normal — to find the variability in the *total* plant costs from a knowledge of the individual items' variability.

References in Chapter 7

1.   Sweeting, J., 1997, *Project Cost Estimating* (IChemE, UK).

Updating estimates

8

8.1 Introduction

It would appear to be an irreversible fact of modern life that the costs of goods and services increase with time. This inflationary effect may slow down or speed up, but the trend is ever upwards. The underlying reason for this is that the costs of raw materials and labour are increasing with time from a variety of commercial, economic and social causes.

In estimating the costs of equipment or process plants, it is therefore necessary to have a means of adjusting the cost of an item at one time to the estimated cost of the same item at another time. This is generally achieved by the use of cost indices using the relation:

$$\frac{C_a}{C_b} = \frac{I_a}{I_b}$$

where,

C_a — cost at time a;
C_b — cost at time b;
I_a — index at time a;
I_b — index at time b.

The method relies on the compilation of cost indices composed from readily available statistics, such as the costs of basic metals and materials, cost and productivity of labour, and other economic indicators. Such statistics are published by many government departments and, in the UK, appear in the publications of the UK Office for National Statistics such as *Monthly Digest of Statistics*, *Economic Trends* and so on.

8.2 Time bases for cost indices

By definition, a cost index will be given the value 100 at the particular date chosen by the index compiler. Thus, two indices with different base dates will, at a particular time, have different numerical values, even though they may be describing the same cost trend.

UK government departments tend to rebase their statistics periodically, usually at five-year intervals, and sometimes they also change the components of these statistics. Once such a change in components occurs, the cost indices utilizing the statistics are no longer fully comparable before and after the change date, and need to be recast for true comparison.

Thus, where a cost index is recast — for example, 1996 = 100 — and it is desired to update from an earlier series of the same index — for example, 1990 = 100 — attempts to merge the two series should be viewed with caution since the bases of the statistics used in making up the index may have changed. This is one of the many reasons why the use of cost indices over time spans of more than about five years may give misleading results.

8.3 Make-up of cost indices

If all the elements and their proportional weightings of the total cost of an item are known, and if time-related statistics for all these elements are available, then a specific cost index for that item can be compiled. However, it would clearly be an impossible task to maintain cost indices for each and every type of plant item, and for the collection of items that make up a process plant.

In practice, compromises have to be made in the selection and weighting of the cost elements in an index. It is the differences in the selections and weightings used in the published indices that can lead to different results for a given location and class of plant.

Thus, in using a cost index, it is extremely important to appreciate the relevance of the selection of cost elements and weightings used in its preparation. It is therefore strongly recommended that the derivation of an index is studied, before applying it for cost estimating purposes.

It is beyond the scope of this Guide to detail the derivations of the many available cost indices, but the general approach is described below.

Most of the published plant cost indices are 'multi-component' indices consisting of about four to six main cost categories, each of which may be further broken down into a number of component parts. For example:

$$I = aM + bE + cC + dS + eO$$

where,

I — cost index;

M, E, C, S, O — indices: M mechanical engineering; E electrical engineering; C civil engineering; S site engineering and O overheads; each calculated from appropriate statistics on materials, labour and other cost elements;

a,b,c,d,e — weightings of the main cost elements within a total plant cost. These weightings are derived from detailed breakdowns of the historical projects and:

$$a + b + c + d + e = 1$$

The main cost elements included and the weightings will be different for each index. It should be noted, in particular, that some indices include factors of 'administration, overheads and profit', while others do not, again emphasizing the need to be aware of the particular make-up of the index in use.

In view of the inherent complexity of these indices, attempts have been made to simplify the procedure by reducing the number of cost elements in the index to a minimum. This approach was proposed by Cran[1] and adopted by *Engineering and Process Economics* in its inaugural issue in 1976, in which there were only two elements:

$$I = 0.3\, I_s + 0.7\, I_L$$

where,

I_S — index of steel prices;

I_L — index of erection labour costs.

Comparing this simple two-part index with several multi-component indices, it was shown that, although in some cases there was divergence, the two-component indices were generally in agreement with, or higher than, the multi-component counterparts. An additional utility of this two-part approach is the ability to make international comparisons on a common basis.

The journal *Process Engineering Economics* (no longer published) maintained this two-component index approach regularly publishing indices for over 30 countries from 1982 to 1988. A further update was provided by Gerrard[2] in 1994.

8.4 UK plant cost indices

The two main multi-component indices published for the UK, which are described in the next sections, have their origins in the work by Eady and Boyd[3] who analysed the erection cost of some 80 chemical, petroleum and petrochemical plants. Four main categories of plant were identified, depending on the occurrence of different types of major plant items. Cost data for the plants were analysed, and weightings determined for the six components which made up the index.

8.4.1 ACE index of erected costs of process plant

The Association of Cost Engineers (ACostE) still publish their index as well as component indices in the journal, *The Cost Engineer*. Now, just one composite index is reported bimonthly and it has the five components listed below:

Mechanical and electrical materials and equipment	50% weighting
Erection labour	25%
Engineering design and administration	15%
Civil and building materials	5%
Civil labour	5%

In Table 8.1, the index has been rounded off to the nearest integer (in the ACostE journal, the data is reported to one decimal place accuracy). At the time of writing, the index has been rebased on 1995 = 100 including the use of new averaged earnings data[4] (to convert to the new base date, divide the figures by 1.26).

8.4.2 Process Engineering plant cost index

The PREDICT Plant Cost Index and its five component indices are published monthly in *Process Engineering*. The weightings for the five components are:

Mechanical	37%
Project overheads	26%
Site engineering	19%
Civil	10%
Electrical	8%

Table 8.1 ACE index of erected costs of process plant costs (1990 = 100)

1979	44	1985	76	1991	106	1997	130
1980	51	1986	80	1992	111	1998	131
1981	57	1987	84	1993	118	1999	131
1982	62	1988	88	1994	122	2000	132 (est)
1983	66	1989	94	1995	126		
1984	71	1990	100	1996	130		

Table 8.2 *Process Engineering* PREDICT plant cost index (1990 = 100)

1979	43	1985	72	1991	105	1997	132
1980	48	1986	76	1992	110	1998	134
1981	52	1987	81	1993	115	1999	135
1982	58	1988	88	1994	120	2000	136 (est)
1983	62	1989	96	1995	125		
1984	67	1990	100	1996	127		

In addition, a useful set of 13 international indices are published for the following countries: Australia, Austria, Belgium, Canada, Denmark, France, Germany, Italy, Japan, Netherlands, Spain, Sweden and USA.

The basis of Table 8.2 is 1990 = 100, again reported to the nearest integer. But the reader should note that this index has just been rebased to 1996 = 100[5] (to convert to the new base date, divide by 1.27).

8.4.3 BEAMA contract price adjustment advisory service

Purchase orders for mechanical or electrical equipment and contracts for site works often state that the price payable will rise or fall with movements in wage rates, costs of materials or other costs. In such cases, contract price adjustment (CPA) clauses are inserted in which formulae and readily available statistics are specified.

The basis for CPA clauses is provided by the British Electrical and Allied Manufacturers Association (BEAMA) who issue their own CPA formulae and labour and material cost indices, including a set for mechanical engineering. Non-members of the Association may, by paying a small annual fee, make full use of the BEAMA CPA Advisory Service and hence receive monthly the current index figures, which, as well as providing data for CPA clauses, also provides useful cost index data.

8.5 USA cost indices

ENR construction index

The Engineering News Record (ENR) Construction Index applies mainly to civil engineering work as it is composed entirely of construction materials and unskilled labour factors. Although it is not really applicable to the process industries, it is mentioned here because it is the oldest of the inflation indices with a base date of 1904 = 100.

CE plant cost index

The *Chemical Engineering* (CE) Plant Cost Index, published monthly by McGraw Hill, is a complex multi-component index[6]. The base date is 1957–59 = 100. (In addition, they publish indices for seven categories of equipment, construction labour, buildings, plus engineering and supervision). Table 8.3 gives annual indices back to 1979.

M&S equipment cost index

The Marshall and Swift (formerly Marshall and Stevens) Equipment Cost Index is an 'all industries' measure comprising a composite value from indices for various industries, (such as cement, chemicals, glass, electrical power and so on.) Again, it is published in *Chemical Engineering* together with the component indices. The base date is 1926 = 100. Table 8.4 gives the annual indices back to 1979.

A further set of indices for eleven categories of air pollution control equipment are also published in *Chemical Engineering*, all based on 1994 (first quarter) = 100. See Vatavuk[7] for the composition of these detailed indices.

Table 8.3 CE plant cost index (1957–59 = 100)

1979	238.7	1985	325.3	1991	361.3	1997	386.5
1980	261.2	1986	318.4	1992	358.2	1998	389.5
1981	297.0	1987	323.8	1993	359.2	1999	390.6
1982	314.0	1988	342.5	1994	368.1	2000	393 (est)
1983	316.9	1989	355.4	1995	381.1		
1984	322.7	1990	357.6	1996	381.7		

Nelson-Farrer refinery construction index

The Nelson-Farrer Refinery Construction Index is published in the first issue of each month of the *Oil and Gas Journal* and is intended to reflect inflation in the construction of refinery units[8,9]. The base date is 1946 = 100 and Table 8.5 gives some annual indices. In addition, the January, April, July and October issues contain information on some 40 categories of process equipment.

Table 8.4 M&S equipment cost index (1926 = 100)

1979	599.4	1985	789.6	1991	930.6	1997	1056.8
1980	659.6	1986	797.6	1992	943.1	1998	1061.9
1981	721.3	1987	813.6	1993	964.2	1999	1068.3
1982	745.6	1988	852.0	1994	993.4	2000	1085 (est)
1983	760.8	1989	895.1	1995	1027.5		
1984	780.4	1990	915.1	1996	1039.2		

Table 8.5 Nelson-Farrer refinery construction index (1946 = 100)

1979	756.6	1985	1074.4	1991	1252.9	1997	1449.2
1980	822.8	1986	1088.9	1992	1277.3	1998	1477.6
1981	903.8	1987	1121.5	1993	1310.8	1999	1497.2
1982	976.9	1988	1164.5	1994	1349.7	2000	1530 (est)
1983	1025.8	1989	1195.9	1995	1392.1		
1984	1061.0	1990	1225.7	1996	1418.9		

8.6 Cost indices for other countries

Considering the number of industrialized and developing countries of the world, surprisingly few outside of the USA and UK produce and publish comprehensive capital cost indices.

- The Netherlands — composite cost index for chemical and similar plants prepared by the Dutch Association of Cost Engineers/Websi[10];
- Germany — cost index for chemical plant prepared by the Technical University of Berlin published as the Kolb and Schulz Index[11];
- South Africa — plant cost index prepared by the Steel and Engineering Industries Federation of South Africa (SEIFSA)[12];
- Canada — The Canadian Government Agency 'Statistics Canada' publishes two cost indices:
  (1) chemical and mineral plant price index;
  (2) chemical and petrochemical plant price index[13].

8.7 Currency translation

The estimation of the cost of a plant item from the known cost of a similar item at an earlier date and different country will involve the use of a *currency translation* as well as a cost index. This is needed when equipment for a project is procured on an international basis.

Where inflationary trends are similar in both countries, it makes little difference which order is employed for the cost indexing and currency translation. However, where the inflationary trends differ, the correct procedure is to apply the cost index first, so that the inflation effect in the country of origin is removed first, and then to correct for currency afterwards. Indeed, it is advisable to apply this procedure in all cases.

Currency exchange rates, as well as being reported in the financial press, are published monthly in the OECD publication, *Main Economic Indicators*, and elsewhere. A listing of some annual average currency exchange rates is given in Table 8.6.

8.8 Location factors

International comparative indices, together with currency translation factors, may be employed to determine 'Location Factors' as proposed by Cran[14, 15].

Location factors relate costs of similar plants in two different locations. It is an empirically derived ratio of plants costs, *that is only valid at a given time and at a specified exchange rate*; for plants similar in function and outline

Table 8.6 Exchange rates against US dollar (annual average rates)

	1979	1990	1991	1992	1993	1994	1995	1996	1997	1998
France (franc)	4.26	5.45	5.64	5.29	5.66	5.55	4.99	5.12	5.84	5.90
Germany (mark)	1.82	1.62	1.66	1.56	1.65	1.62	1.43	1.51	1.73	1.76
Holland (guilder)	2.01	1.82	1.87	1.76	1.86	1.82	1.61	1.69	1.95	1.98
Italy (lire)	830	1200	1240	1230	1570	1610	1630	1540	1700	1740
Japan (yen)	220	145	134	127	111	102	94	109	121	131
Norway (krone)	5.07	6.26	6.48	6.21	7.09	7.06	6.34	6.46	7.07	7.55
UK (pound)	0.47	0.56	0.57	0.57	0.67	0.65	0.63	0.64	0.61	0.60

All exchange rates are shown based on their equivalence to $1 and represent an average value for the stated year

specification but that are not necessarily identical. For example, for a plant that costs $11 million in the USA in 1979 when the equivalent plant cost £5 million in the UK, at the exchange rate of $2.12/£ then:

$$LF_{US/UK}, 1979 = \frac{\$11 \text{ million}}{\$2.12 / £} \times £5 \text{ million}$$

$$= 1.04$$

or in general:

$$LF_{US/UK}, \text{ given date} = \frac{\$C_{US}}{£C_{UK}} \times \frac{ER\,\$}{£}, \text{ all at the same date}$$

where,

LF — location factor;

C — cost;

ER — exchange rate.

Objective international plant cost comparisons are rarely carried out, and since costs, exchange rates and location factors all vary with time at different rates in different locations, an analytical approach to derivation of location factors is not often practicable. Instead, an empirical approach gives the values quoted in Table 8.7, from Bridgwater[16]. These have been validated from a variety of sources in the chemical industry and process plant contractors and give location factors relative to both the UK and USA in 1979 at the exchange rate prevailing at that time.

In an interesting article[17], the results of the ACostE study of the relative costs of building a similar plant in a number of locations were reported alongside industrial data from ICI.

The ACostE figures were:

In 1988, Q1, if LF = 1 for UK then:

France = 0.7,

Holland = 0.8,

Mexico = 0.72,

Norway = 1.38,

USA = 0.77

whereas ICI suggested in 1989, Q3, if LF for UK = 1 then:

France = 0.78,	Brazil = 1.12,
Holland = 0.91,	India = 1.03,
Mexico = 0.76,	Italy = 0.83,
Norway = 1.55,	Japan = 1.01,
USA = 0.82	

One approach to the calculation of a cost of the plant at a new location at a different time is:

- to deflate the base cost back to '1979*' in the original currency, in the original location;
- then convert at the '1979' location factor and '1979' exchange rate to the new country and new currency;
- and finally to escalate to the present or selected date, in the new country and new currency.

* use the base date for the location factor being used. In the above, it is assumed that the data comes from Table 8.7.

For more comprehensive multi-component methods for estimating plant location factors, see Gallagher[18] and Miller[19]. It can be argued that in the free markets of today, the same plant will cost the same (at the prevailing exchange rate) in all industrialized countries.

Table 8.7 Location factors in 1979 for chemical plants of similar function

Country		UK = 1.0	USA = 1.0
Australia		1.4	1.3
Austria		1.1	1.0
Belgium		1.1	1.0
Canada		1.25	1.15
Central Africa		(2.0)	(2.0)
Central America		1.1	1.1
China	Imported element	1.2	1.1
	Indigenous element	0.5	0.55
Denmark		1.1	1.0
Eire		0.9	0.8
Finland		1.3	1.2
France		1.05	0.95
Germany (West)		1.1	1.0
Greece		1.0	0.9
Holland		1.1	1.0
India	Imported element	2.0	1.8
	Indigenous element	0.6	0.55
Italy		1.0	0.9
Japan		1.0	0.9
Libya		2.7	2.4
Malaysia		0.9	0.8
Middle East		1.9	1.7
Newfoundland		1.3	1.2
New Zealand		1.4	1.3
North Africa	Imported element	1.2	1.1
	Indigenous element	0.8	0.75
Norway		1.2	1.1
Portugal		0.8	0.75
South Africa		1.25	1.15
South America (North)		(1.5)	(1.35)
South America (South)		(2.5)	(2.25)
Spain	Imported element	1.2	1.1
	Indigenous element	0.8	0.75
Sweden		1.2	1.1
Switzerland		1.2	1.1
Turkey		0.8	0.7
UK		1.0	0.9
USA		1.1	1.0
Yugoslavia		1.0	0.9

Parameters: identical function. Industrial centre and major import centre within 100 miles. Above 100 miles, add 10% for each 1000 miles apart.

(This table is based on Table 2 from Bridgwater, A.V., 1979, International construction cost factors, *Chemical Engineering*, 86(24): 119–121.)

8.9 Cautionary notes

It will be apparent from the earlier sections of this chapter that the use of cost indices for updating costs has many pitfalls. A lack of awareness of these dangers can lead to unnecessary inaccuracies in cost estimating. Care must therefore be exercised in using the various available cost indices. In particular:

- The cost index which is most relevant to the particular situation must be used — be aware of the derivations and statistical bases of your index.

- Indices can only reflect 'today's' cost of 'yesterday's' plant. They cannot take into account advances in technology, higher standards of environmental control, operational or construction safety.

- Where construction conditions deviate from 'average mainland construction conditions', either for the reference plant or the plant under consideration, due allowances must be made for this in the cost estimate.

- Site clearance, contractor's overheads and profit, and client's costs are not always included in the indices. Trends in these costs may differ from those indicated by the index.

- Indices are generally *cost* indices and not *price* indices. Prices of plants will be affected by the business environment and commercial pressures, as well as by cost levels.

- Use of cost indices to update *plant* costs over periods longer than five years should be viewed with caution due to factors such as changes in legislation, productivity and technology. Individual *item* costs can be updated over a longer period but, of course, the more recent the data the better.

References for Chapter 8

1. Cran, J., 1976, Cost indices, *Engineering and Process Economics*, 1: 13–23.
2. Gerrard, A.M., 1994, International cost indices, *The Chemical Engineer*, 557: 18.
3. Eady, C.E. and Boyd, N.G., 1964, Indices of erected costs of chemical and applied plant, *Chem Proc Eng*, 45(3).
4. Anon, 1999, *The Cost Engineer*, 37(5): 26.
5. Anon, 1999, PREDICT Indices: A time to revisit, review and reformat, *Process Engineering*, 80(5): 19.
6. Matley, J., 1982, CE Plant Cost Index – Revised, *Chem Eng*, April 19, 153.
7. Vatavuk, W.M., 1995, Air pollution control, escalate equipment costs, *Chem Eng*, 88–95.
8. Farrar, G.L., 1985, How Nelson cost indices are compiled, *Oil and Gas Journal*, December 30, 145.
9. Farrar, G.L., 1999, How Nelson-Farrer indexes of chemical costs have changed, *Oil and Gas Journal*, July 5, 68.

10. Helter, B.K., 1974, A cost index for plant construction in the Netherlands, *Proceedings of the Third International Cost Engineering Symposium, London,* paper reference F5.

11. Schulze, J., 1974, Development of a cost index for chemical plant in Western Germany, *Proceedings of the Third International Cost Engineering Symposium, London,* paper reference F6.

12. Anon, 1985, Substituting parallel indices, *Process Engineering,* October, 13.

13. Anon, 1986, Canadian plant price indices, *Process Engineering,* March, 13.

14. Cran, J., 1976, EPE Plant Cost Indices International (1970 = 100), *Engineering and Process Economics,* 1: 109–112.

15. Cran, J., 1976, EPE plant cost indices international, *Engineering and Process Economics,* 1: 321–323.

16. Bridgwater, A.V., 1979, International construction cost location factor, *Chem Eng,* 5 November, 119–121.

17. Soloman, G., 1990, Location factors, *The Cost Engineer,* 28(2).

18. Gallagher, J.T., 1969, Efficient estimating of worldwide plant costs, *Chem Eng,* 76, (June 2), 196–198.

19. Miller, A.C., 1979, Converting construction costs from one country to another, *Chem Eng,* July 2, 89.

Sources of cost information

9

9.1 Survey of sources

This Guide is concerned with the principles of capital cost estimation and no attempt has been made to provide a complete handbook of cost data, although some useful graphs are included in Chapter 7. It has been shown, however, that the estimator must have access to comprehensive and reasonably accurate cost information if well-founded cost estimates are to be prepared. Contracting organizations and many of the larger chemical manufacturing companies are able to justify having fully staffed and equipped estimating departments. Such departments are responsible not only for estimating, but also for collating and updating the necessary cost data.

There are a large number of companies, however, who cannot justify full-time estimating departments. Engineers are often required to make their own estimates based on experience and cost information retrieval. The methods adopted to prepare a cost estimate depend to a large extent on the degree of definition of the project under consideration and the form and source of cost data available, as discussed in Chapters 3 and 4. A number of sources of cost data are available to the engineer faced with the task of preparing a cost estimate in addition to the data and techniques described previously, and a guide to such data is presented below.

9.2 Suppliers' detailed quotations

For main equipment items, the most accurate costs are obtained from suppliers' quotations submitted against detailed specifications. If the normal practice of obtaining quotations from several suppliers is followed, even this method may result in a wide spread of quoted costs, requiring detailed technical and economic analysis before selection is made. In most cases quotations are subject to limited life, transport is charged extra at cost and, if items are imported, they are subject to tax and duty and the vagaries of fluctuating exchange rates.

9.3 Suppliers' budget quotations

The above method is time-consuming and is usually only applicable for project execution after authorization. At the project study stage, however, suppliers will frequently be willing to give budget prices, rapidly and without commitment, which, in general, will be more accurate than published data. The same caveats apply as in Section 9.2.

9.4 Company records

Company records of past projects and purchases usually contain extensive and useful cost information. If such information is systematically analysed, recorded and filed, together with a suitable retrieval system, this forms a good basis for cost information. In many companies, however, cost information is buried with the project records, discouraging any search for cost data on a particular piece of equipment. Efficient and cost-conscious companies often analyse and record cost data, and maintain a comprehensive database of both historic and 'target' costs — the latter being the probable current price of the item concerned including consideration of market forces. This is potentially more valuable and accurate than other sources since it will reflect the current market situation of supply and demand.

9.5 Trade literature

Costs for standard items of equipment such as valves, pipe fittings and so on are often circulated, or published in trade journals by traders in these items as part of their sales and advertising efforts. The usefulness of these lists is often negated by being undated, and the practice of publishing price lists has declined in recent times.

9.6 Unit pricing literature

Unit prices for measured work are published annually. For example, see Spon's *Mechanical and Electrical Services Price Book*[1] and *Laxton's Building Price Book*[2]. Other useful sources of similar cost data are periodicals such as *Civil Engineering* and *Building Trades Journal*. These are intended principally for the building, civil and structural engineering trades where Bills of Quantities are drawn up and priced. They do, however, contain considerable cost data of general use, such as approximate cost of different types of building on an area or volumetric basis with Spon's work devoting a chapter to process plant.

9.7 Technical literature and textbooks

One of the largest sources of generalized cost data for process plants is the chemical and allied industry technical press. Cost information has been published for most equipment items and project cost elements of the type encountered in a chemical project. However, this information is widely spread in the literature. A deficiency of this type of published cost data is that, in the interest of presenting the data in a concise or correlated form, the specifications of the items are often not fully defined. Another drawback is that much of the data relates to costs in the USA. However, with judicious use, published cost data can provide a reasonable basis for cost estimation.

9.8 Personal cost books

Many engineers keep their own cost data books into which they jot down pertinent items of cost information gathered over the years.

9.9 Government departments

Several government departments maintain statistics of wages, productivity and material costs which are of value in compiling general cost indices and cost indices for specific projects. Similar data for other countries are often available from applicable embassies, trade delegations and so on.

9.10 Computer data

A number of packages have been developed for capital cost estimating by the contracting industry and by some of the major chemical manufacturers, and a few of these are commercially available. For example, see the Icarus website (www.icarus-us.com) for details on their products in this field.

9.11 Data sources

For capital cost data, a few sources of information are included here. In the UK, the journal *Process Engineering* offers a monthly feature on process economics, which also includes their set of cost indices. *The Cost Engineer* (UK) and *Cost Engineering* (USA) journals are also worth looking at. *Chemical Engineering*, *Oil and Gas Journal* and *Hydrocarbon Processing* often feature articles on cost matters.

The American Association of Cost Engineers (www.aacei.org) also run a yearly conference whose transactions contain a wide variety of topics. The biannual International Cost Engineering Congress (www.icoste.org) is another useful source of published information. The IChemE Education Subject Group website also holds information on material and utility costs, which is accessed via the IChemE website (www.icheme.org).

Text books with important cost sections include Coulson and Richardson's *Chemical Engineering*[3] and Garrett's *Chemical Engineering Economics*[4]. Brennan's *Process Industry Economics*[5] contains a useful and up-to-date literature survey of cost sources.

References in Chapter 9

1. Langdon, D. (ed), 1999, *Spon's Mechanical and Electrical Services Price Book*, 30th edn (E and FN Spon, UK).
2. Johnson, V.B. (ed), 1999, *Laxton's Building Price Book* (Butterworth-Heinemann, UK).
3. Coulson and Richardson, 1999, *Chemical Engineering*, Sinnott, R.K. (ed), vol 6 (Butterworth and Heinemann, UK).
4. Garrett, D.E., 1989, *Chemical Engineering Economics* (Van Nostrand Reinhold, USA).
5. Brennan, D., 1998, *Process Industry Economics* (IChemE, UK).

Glossary

Battery limits

The line of demarcation surrounding work to be covered by a project sometimes used to define the division of responsibility between, for example, an employer and contractor.

CIF

Cost Insurance and Freight are the responsibility of the seller of the goods to an agreed destination, but unloading is the buyer's responsibility unless specified 'CIF landed'.

Contingency

An allowance for uncertain elements of cost particularly in fixed investment estimates, which previous experience has shown likely to occur. (May include allowance for inflation but this is best identified separately in an estimate.)

Cost code (code of accounts)

A series of alphabetical and/or numerical symbols, each of which represents a descriptive title in expenditure classification.

Cost element

Any portion of an expenditure which can be separately classified.

Cost indices

A series of numbers recording changes in values since some predetermined date, when the base value was equal to 100.

Delivered equipment cost

The price of item which includes delivery to the site. Generally excludes unloading, except for loose materials delivered by a tipper-type vehicle such as sand, shale and so on.

Direct costs

The cost of all inputs directly attributable to the provision of a new capital asset or, in the case of manufacturing, to the making of the product.

Escalation

The rise (fall) of prices over a given time period or the project life. This may be due to a change in the purchasing power of the currency, which is termed *inflation*. But in addition to this, errors and omissions in the scope of the project can have a major effect on the growth of the final total cost of the project.

Exponent

The power to which size is raised in a cost correlation.

Ex-works

The seller's responsibility is to make the goods available at the premises for loading and transportation by the buyer.

Factored estimate

A forecast of project cost made by applying multiplying factors to the major items' costs in order to evaluate the minor components.

FAS

The supply of goods by the seller 'Free Alongside Ship' — that is, on the quay or in lighters — when the risk of loss of damage passes to the buyer.

Field costs

Project expenditure directly related to activities at the construction site.

FOB

'Free on Board' means that the seller is required to place the goods on board a ship; but note that the risk of loss or damage to the goods is transferred from the seller to the buyer when the goods pass the ship's rail.

Freight

The charge for the transportation of goods from a supplier to a purchaser, which can be paid by either party, according to agreement.

Grass-roots plant

A complete installation, including site preparation, and auxiliary facilities erected onto a virgin site.

Greenfield site
A plot of land in its natural state, upon which it is proposed to locate a new plant or facility.

Home office costs
The general administration and office operations' costs and expenses of a business undertaking (but normally excluding factory costs and site expenses). May comprise any or all of the following cost centres:
- engineering design and drafting;
- consultant's fees and/or management costs;
- contractor's fee and/or profit;
- purchasing;
- legal costs;
- general overheads;
- procurement and expedition.

Indirect cost
An expense which cannot be directly allocated, but which can be apportioned to or absorbed by direct cost centres or units.

Inflation
An increase in spending not associated with an expansion in the volume of goods or services obtained — that is, a change in the purchasing power of money. It has the effect that the same item costs more in the future.

Inflation index (or cost index)
(a) A series of numbers recording the change in prices relative to those at some past date, when the index was 100.
(b) Historical time series maintained by the Government and others which approximate the change (usually loss) in the purchasing value of money in a particular segment of the economy, usually based on an index of 100 at a specified time.

Installed cost
The value of capital equipment, plus the expense of erecting and fixing it to permanent foundations.

Lang factors
A set of multiplying numbers evolved by Lang for converting the delivered cost of equipment into the cost of installed plant and, ultimately, the cost of a completed project.

Main plant items

The major items such as the vessels, exchangers, machines, mechanical handling equipment and electrical motors, including installed spares to be positioned within the battery limits.

Off-site facilities

Auxiliary equipment and services located outside the battery limits of a production plant which provide support for the process units — for example, tank farms, effluent plants and so on.

Overhead

A cost or expense inherent in the performing of an operation — that is, engineering, construction, operating or manufacturing — which cannot be directly and solely identified with a part of the work, product or asset and, therefore, must be allocated on some arbitrary basis, believed to be equitable, or handled as a business expense independent of the volume of production.

Packaged plant

An assemblage of machinery or other equipment which can form a self-contained process unit to be installed by the vendor and whose cost therefore includes the cost of the equipment and supplying it and the cost of installing it on prepared foundations.

Salvage value

The value which can be recovered from equipment or other facilities when taken out of processing use and sold to an outside party. Usually assumed as a value net of removal and selling costs.

Scaling factors

The relationship between cost and size used in estimating new process equipment, where these are often expressed by the equation:

$$\frac{Cost_1}{Cost_2} = \left(\frac{Size_1}{Size_2}\right)^n$$

When the exponent is $n = 0.6$, this is known as the six-tenths rule.

Utilities

The permanent equipment for electricity, steam, water, effluent treatment and so on installed in a building or works as distinct from the main process plant.

Working capital

In this Guide, the term is applied to the part of capital which is invested in stock, work-in-progress, finished products and the cash requirements necessary to pay current salaries, wages and so on to finance sales on credit terms.

It is the part of a trading company's assets which can be readily converted into cash, consisting of the difference between current assets and current liabilities. This working capital is normally expected to be recovered without loss on completion of each project period, to enable profitable trading to continue without affecting the fixed capital, such as plant, land and buildings.

Index